MICHAEL FORSTER
ACT TWO
45 BIBLE DRAMAS

Kevin
Mayhew

First published in 1996 by
KEVIN MAYHEW LTD
Rattlesden
Bury St Edmunds
Suffolk IP30 0SZ

0 1 2 3 4 5 6 7 8 9

ISBN 0 86209 850 5
Catalogue No 1500056

Cover illustration by Darren Regan
Edited by Stephen Haddelsey
Typesetting by Louise Hill
Printed in Great Britain

Foreword

Most, although not all, of these dramas are taken from my school assembly books *Wonderful World!* and *God's Wonderful People*, and here presented separately for use in the church context where those books may not be appropriate. All of them are based upon stories in *The Word for All Age Worship*.

As users of the earlier books will know, all the stories have been imaginatively rewritten while retaining and emphasising the original meaning. I hope that this not only makes them more enjoyable in themselves but also, in many cases, brings out other dimensions of the biblical texts. They are intended to be fun, but to make serious points. To this end, the dialogue is deliberately modern, and often colloquial, in order to make the characters as recognisably like real people as possible, rather than dim figures from the distant past, speaking in conventional religious language. Some of the stories have been transposed into the present day, all in the hope both of making the dramas entertaining and of holding people's attention so that the essential points can be conveyed and remembered. It is of course open to individual readers to adapt the words to a style which best suits their own personalities or situations.

Each drama also includes some actions (indicated by a •) to involve the audience or congregation. It would be as well to give some thought to how these are to be included and led, before the day itself. The dramas may be enhanced, and individual talents recognised, through the use of dance, mime, simple costumes and sets.

I believe that 'all age worship' should be what its name suggests, which means that as far as possible it should be both accessible and satisfying for people of every age. So while I hope that these dramas will communicate well with quite young children, they also have other layers of meaning which may speak to older children and adults as well.

It has been a highly enjoyable task to produce this book; I hope it may be at least equally enjoyable to use, enabling people of all ages and at all stages of the Christian journey to learn and worship together.

MICHAEL FORSTER

Contents

Let it Be

Based on Genesis 1

Narrator Before God made the world, it was very, very dark.

God Let there be light!

Narrator And suddenly, there was light everywhere.

God That's pretty good, but it wouldn't do to have it always. There. That's the day, and I'll call that the night

Narrator So the evening came, and then the morning, and that was the very first day. But things were still pretty messy! So God did some sorting out.

God There. I'll call this part 'heaven'.

Narrator By that time it was evening, and after that came another morning: the second day, but there was an awful lot of water sloshing about in the world

God Let's make a bit of dry land. I'll call the dry bits 'earth' and the watery bits 'sea'. My Word, that's good! Now, let's see what this earth can produce! Give me some plants! Give me some seeds! Give me some fruit!

Narrator Before long, the earth was covered with wonderful green plants, and brightly coloured fruit: red strawberries, yellow bananas – all sorts of things.

God Well, bless me! This is really good!

Narrator The evening had come again. Then came the morning, and that was the third day. The earth was looking pretty spectacular. So God looked around at the sky.

God I'd better spruce this up a bit. Lets have some stars, and planets around here. And they'd better move round in circles to mark the seasons – otherwise we'll end up with May blossom in November or something equally silly. We'll have bright light for the day, and a dimmer one at night. Well upon my Word – that's a good day's work!

Narrator Now the fourth day had gone. The earth looked great, but the sea was looking a bit empty.

God Let's see what the sea can do. Give me lots of animals – great big sea monsters, and whales and sharks, and octopuses. And let's have some birds in the air as well.

Narrator Straight away, there were fish and birds everywhere.

- The fish *swam*
- The eels *wriggled*
- And the birds *flapped their wings*

God That's right – make yourselves at home, and let's have lots of you – I want plenty of life in the world!

Narrator When morning came, God looked at the earth again.

God Come on – let's have some life around here! Don't leave it all to the sea.

Narrator And so there were animals – everything from dinosaurs to dingoes! And God was pleased – but not that pleased!

God What would really top it off would be people. Human beings, made to be like me, able to love and be loved, to be my special friends. We could do things together. They would be the best of all the things I've made.

Narrator So God made men and women; he made them able to love, and able to think.

God Come and be my special friends. Look, I've given you great things – plants and fruit and rocks, wonderful colours, and everything you could ever need. Look after it well, and work with me to make it even better.

Narrator God was pleased with everything he had made

God Even though I say it myself, it's pretty terrific! A good week's work by any standards. Bless me! Is that the time? I think I'll have a day off.

Snake in the Grass

Based on Genesis 3

Narrator Cecil the snake was hiding in some bushes in the Garden of Eden, plotting his revenge.

Cecil I sssay! What a liberty! I ought to be in charge here, not the humans. After all, I was here firssst! Thessse new animalsss! 'Adam and Eve' – they're sssilly names to ssstart with. They think they own the plassse! I think I'll have sssome fun.

Narrator Cecil squirmed up close to Eve.

Eve Ooh! You didn't half frighten me.

Cecil I'm ssso sssorry to have ssscared you. I'm Sssessssil the ssserpent, and I wanted to sssay welcome to thisss Garden of Eden.

Eve Very kind of you, I'm sure. No offence meant.

Cecil None taken. Have you sssampled sssome of the delicasssiesss around here? Sssome of the fruit is sssimply ssscrupmtiousss – essspesssially that tree in the sssentre of the garden.

Eve God said we mustn't eat from it or we'll die.

Cecil That'sss sssilly! God jussst doesssn't want you to be clever like him, that'sss all.

Eve You mean, if I eat that I'll be as wise as God?

Cecil Sssertain as sssunshine in Ssseptember! Try it – itsss sssensssasssional!

Narrator Well, the fruit looked tempting, and Eve thought that to be like God would be wonderful. So she ate the fruit. Then her husband Adam came along.

Adam You haven't eaten that, have you?

Eve Of course I have. I knew God was only trying to frighten us – here, have some.

Narrator Adam hesitated a moment, and then took the fruit and bit into it. Just as he was enjoying it, Eve shrieked so that he nearly swallowed the pips.

Eve   We haven't got any clothes on!

Narrator   Now the silly thing is they'd never bothered with clothes until they ate the fruit. But now, for some strange reason, they were terribly embarrassed. Then they heard the sound of God's voice.

God   Adam, where are you?

Narrator   Adam and Eve were frightened.

- They *crouched down low*
- they *covered their faces*
- and they *peeped through their fingers*

God   Found you! Have you eaten from that tree?

Adam   Um – er – It's not my fault. Eve made me do it.

God   Oh, that's right, blame the woman for it. After all, you might as well start as you mean to go on!

Eve   Don't blame me – Cecil made me do it!

God   What? Cecil the Snake? But you're supposed to be better and more intelligent than him.

Cecil   *(Aside)* Huh! That shows what you know!

God   Well, that's torn it! I hoped you'd all work together – people, animals, everything – but you've ruined all that. Well, you can get out of this garden, for a start. Go and work for your livings. And as for you, Cecil, since you seem to enjoy saying esses, I'll fix it so that that's all you do say from now on.

Narrator   Cecil was so embarrassed that he just lay down on his stomach and crawled away. And that's how he has been ever since. Men, women and animals carry on fighting and blaming one another, and no-one ever wants to admit being wrong. No wonder we make ourselves unhappy!

Oh Brother!

Based on Genesis 4:1-12

Narrator   Adam and Eve had two sons, called Cain and Abel Sometimes the boys played together, and at other times they would argue and fight, and they often used to get jealous of one another.

Eve   Adam, I worry about those two. One of these days one of them's going to get badly hurt in their arguments.

Adam   Oh don't exaggerate! You worry too much. It's just the way children are. We were young once, you know.

Eve   No we weren't. That's the problem with being the first people God made.

Adam   There you are, then! What d'you know about children? Leave them alone.

Narrator   That wasn't very helpful of Adam, was it? Well, Cain and Abel grew up from children into young men and they were still quarrelling and getting jealous of each other.

Eve   They'll never survive if they carry on like this.

Adam   I know. We'll teach them separate trades, so they can't compete.

Narrator   So that's what they did.

- Cain learned to *scatter seeds*
- and to *clip hedges*
- Abel learned to *shear sheep*

Narrator   Even when they grew up into men, the boys wouldn't stop fighting. The real trouble happened when Abel's sheep had their first lambs.

Abel   I'll give some of the lambs to God, to say thank you.

Narrator	Straight away, Cain had a bad thought.
Cain	I'll make God like me more than he likes Abel.
Narrator	Abel brought some beautiful young lambs and offered them to God. Then he heard a mean voice behind him.
Cain	Come on, God – get a load of this, then! I've brought you some wheat, some bread, carrots, potatoes, apples, pears – better than a few silly little lambs, eh!
Narrator	God did not like this one little bit.
God	Abel just wanted to give me a present, but you did it to get one up on him. So I like Abel's gift best.
Cain	*(Aside)* I'll get Abel for this! Just see if I don't. *(To Abel)* How about a nice walk in the country?
Narrator	As soon as they got out of sight of the house, Cain picked up a big sharp stone, and killed Abel with it. Then he turned to go home
God	Cain, where's your brother?
Cain	Who am I – his keeper?
God	That's a silly question. Abel's never needed a keeper. But he's often wanted a proper brother.
Cain	I'm his brother.
God	Exactly. Now where's Abel? You've killed him, haven't you? Well, you can't face your parents now, so you're going to have to go and live somewhere else. And for the rest of your life you'll be a guilty person, on the run.
Narrator	So that's how it turned out. How Cain wished he'd listened to God and learnt to control his temper!

Rabbles and Babbles

Based on Genesis 11:1-9

Narrator A long, long time ago, everyone in the world spoke the same language – until Barnaby had his bright idea.

Barnaby You know, Johnny, if we all worked together we could do anything – even climb right up to heaven!

Johnny That's ridiculous. How do you know heaven's up there? It might be more complicated than you think.

Barnaby Oh, don't be stupid! Heaven's got to be up there; it's not down here, so that's the only place left. And where d'you think all that light comes from?

Johnny I know – but things aren't always as they seem.

Barnaby You're a philosopher

Johnny That's a rotten thing to say!

Barnaby Look, it's very simple. What you see is what there is. Don't make things complicated by asking unnecessary questions. This is earth, and heaven's up there. That's how it looks, and that's how it is.

Narrator Johnny didn't like arguing with Barnaby, because he always felt so inferior; Barnaby seemed to know so much, and to be so confident, and Johnny always ended up feeling silly. Still, he tried again.

Johnny Perhaps God doesn't want us to climb up to heaven – if that's where it is. Perhaps that's why we can't see it.

Barnaby Don't be stupid – we have a duty to use all the knowledge we have. That's what God expects. So whatever we're capable of doing must be right.

Johnny *(Aside to audience)* I'm capable of punching him on the nose, but that doesn't mean it would be right!

Narrator So nearly everyone set to work. Johnny didn't join in because he thought it was wrong, and Barnaby didn't either, because he thought he was too important.

Barnaby I'm an ideas man. I must save my creative energy, and let less important people do the actual work.

Narrator Surprisingly, most of the other people joined in. They were very impressed by Barnaby's confidence, and thought Johnny was a very silly man.

- so the architect *drew the plans*
- the stone masons *hammered and chiselled*
- the carpenters *sawed the wood*

Narrator God knew what was happening, and he didn't like it.

God I didn't put people on earth so that they could spend all their time trying to get back to heaven! These people are obsessed! They never play with their children, or look after their elderly relations. I'll teach them a lesson, and give them something else to think about.

Narrator So it was that, one morning, Barnaby got up and went out as usual to find an unwelcome surprise awaiting him. He'd have known about it earlier if he'd listened to his wife, but he never did that – he just used to get up and rush straight out to see how the tower was getting on. As he got near to the tower, he heard a loud babbling – lots of people all shouting and yelling at one another.

Barnaby You're supposed to be building this tower, not gossiping amongst yourselves – now get on with it!

Narrator Soon, they were all shouting at one another and getting nowhere because they were all speaking different languages! No-one could understand anybody else at all!

Barnaby Now the tower will never get finished.

Narrator God is still trying to teach us that heaven isn't in the sky; the way to find heaven is to care about other people, and learn to understand each other. And all this time later, we're still not very good at it!

Don't Ask Me!

Based on Exodus 3:1-4:17

Narrator	Moses was having a nice quiet life. The rest of the Hebrew people were terribly unhappy, because they were slaves in Egypt, but Moses had escaped from that and he was working as a shepherd. One day, he was out minding the sheep when he noticed something strange. A bush nearby seemed to be on fire, except that it wasn't going all black and shrivelled the way bushes normally do when they burn. So he took a closer look. Then he had the shock of his life – he heard a voice.
God	Hey! Moses! Over here.
Moses	What's that? Surely, not the bush talking!
God	Come over here, Moses. I want to talk to you. But take your shoes off, first, because this is holy ground.
Narrator	Holy ground! Of course! It was God who was speaking. Mind you, it might have been better if it had been the bush; when God gives people visions he usually has a job for them to do! Moses did as he was told; he took off his shoes and went closer.
God	That's better. Now we can talk properly. I've been watching what's been going on in Egypt.
Moses	*(Aside)* Lucky him! I haven't seen a cabaret in years.
God	Not that! I'm going to set the slaves free – and you're going to help me.
Moses	I hope you're not going to ask me to get involved in politics, because I don't think it mixes with religion.
God	Oh, not that cop-out again! If you had any idea how often I've heard that! Look, people are suffering, and I care! Go and see Pharaoh and tell him to let them go.
Moses	Go and see who? And tell him what? I can't do that! It's all right for you, but I have to live in this world! Anyway, you need a good orator – an experienced politician. I just know what'll happen when I get in

front of the king: I'll get all tongue tied – that's if he doesn't cut it out first.

God   Trust me, Moses. I'll be right with you the whole time.

Narrator   Things weren't going Moses' way. So he tried to think of another approach.

- he *scratched his head*
- and then he *shook his head*
- suddenly he *snapped his fingers.* Got it!

Moses put on his most reasonable and worldly-wise voice – a bit like a politician who's being given a hard time by an interviewer on the radio.

Moses   Well of course, God, the reality is that these people have never heard of you. They've been in slavery all their lives, and I'm afraid we need to face up to the situation as it really is – they've forgotten you. I mean, what am I going to say if they ask who you are? Have you got a name?'

God   Oh no you don't, Moses! You can't put a label on me, like a plant or an animal. I'm greater than any name you could think of. *I* decide who and what I am, and I will be whoever I choose – go and tell the slaves that!

Moses   But no-one's going to listen to me! I'm a terrible speaker – you ask my wife about that, she'll tell you! No-one will take notice of me. Look, I've got a nice home, a lovely wife, and a good, steady job. That's the kind of bloke I am. I'm not into—

God   If you mention politics again, you'll regret it! I care about people – and if you're a friend of mine you will, as well. Take Aaron with you – he can talk.

Moses   That's true! He could talk both the humps off a Bactrian camel, could Aaron.

God   That's settled then. Now go and get Aaron, and let's get cracking. We're going to set the people free!

You Can't get Water from a Stone
Based on Exodus 17:2-7

Narrator   Remember Moses? He was the man who helped God set the Israelites free. The trouble was that the people thought he was going to solve all their problems in one go. And when he didn't, they all moaned at Moses.

Moses   I'm fed up with this, God. I never wanted the job in the first place – I told you I wasn't up to it.

God   I know you're not, but I am – so trust me. Anyway, you've got visitors and they don't look very happy.

Moses   Oh, no! It's that Simon character. He's been making trouble ever since we left Egypt.

Simon   Hey, Moses! We want a word with you. We're thirsty.

Moses   Well, stop shouting, then, or you'll make it worse.

Simon   Don't you get clever – we've had enough of that.

Moses   Look, I said we'd find the Promised Land, and we will.

Simon   When?

Moses   I don't know.

Simon   All right, then – where is it?'

Moses   Don't ask me – how should I know?

Simon   Well you're the one who's leading us there!

Moses   Don't be idiotic, Simon. God's the one who's leading us, and as long as he knows where we're going that's all that matters.

Simon   You're mad, you are. Just because you hear strange voices, you think God's talking to you. All right, then – if you've got God on your side, what about a bit of water? That's not much to ask, is it?

Narrator   Then all the others started to join in.

(Have a few children primed to lead the barracking.)

- Simon: What do we want?
- Children: *Water!*
- Simon: When do we want it?
- Children: *Now!*
- *(Repeat ad lib)*

Moses   Okay, God, you told me to trust you. Now what?

God   Simple – get some water out of one or those rocks.

Moses   What! Get water out of a stone? That's impossible.

God   Look, Moses, I could get blood out of a stone if I wanted to, but water will do for now. Stop arguing and do as I say. Hit one of those rocks with your stick.

Narrator Moses was certainly ready to hit something! He raised his stick and brought it down hard on the rock.

Simon   Temper, temper! That won't get you anywhere.

Narrator A tiny crack appeared in the rock, and a trickle of water came out. Everyone ran forward, fighting to get the first drink in case there wasn't enough to go round. Just as they got to the rock, there was a great, thunderous crash and it split wide open as a rush of water came pouring out. Simon was closest, and ended up rolling around in a big muddy puddle. Every time he tried to stand up someone pushed him down again. He had wet sand in his clothes, in his shoes, in his hair, in his ears and in his mouth. And it tasted horrible!

Moses   There you are, Simon – all the water you could want. That'll teach you not to complain.

Narrator But it didn't.

A Little Yellow Idol

Based on Exodus 32:1-24

Narrator   Moses was up a mountain, praying.

Moses   It's not fair, God. You're the boss, but I get moaned at.

God   That's the way it is. They can't see me, so they have a go at my friends. Anyway, you'd better get to work. I've got a few rules to help you all live properly, and I want you to write them down on stone.

Moses   That's hard work. Can't I use clay or something?

God   *(Sternly)* Stone. This has got to last.

Narrator   Meanwhile, down at the bottom of the mountain, Simon was stirring up trouble. But then, Simon always did. And at this particular moment, he'd got a crowd round him and was having the time of this life!

Simon   We were better off as slaves!

Children   Yeah!

Simon   Moses is a fool!

Children   Yeah!

Simon   Couldn't find his way along a straight line if it was signposted!

Children   Yeah!

Narrator   That got Simon confused, because he wasn't sure whether they should really have shouted 'no'!

Simon   Well, Aaron – you're Moses' brother, aren't you – what are you going to do about it?

Aaron   All right – collect all the people's earrings, bangles, bracelets, anything at all that's made of gold. While that's happening, I want two volunteers to help me make a mould. You and you will do.

Narrator   Up the mountain, God had finished talking to Moses.

God   I think you'd better go. Things are getting out of hand.

Narrator   When Moses got down the mountain, he couldn't believe his eyes! There was a big party going on, round a golden statue of a calf.

- Some were *banging the drums*
- some were *blowing their trumpets*
- and some were *waving their arms about*

Narrator   Moses didn't mind that – or the dancing and singing. It was the statue he objected to. He was so mad that he threw down and smashed the stone tablets he'd been working on.

Moses   Hey! Aaron! What's that thing?

Aaron   Oh – well – er – it was the funniest thing. You'll laugh when I tell you. We just put our gold on the fire, and out came this calf.

Moses   I'm not swallowing that – but you are.

Aaron   Eh?

Moses   Grind it down into dust, mix it with water and drink it.

Aaron   You don't mean it!

Moses   Oh yes I do. If that thing is a god then it must be full of life and goodness Now you can find out.

Narrator   And Moses made them drink every drop! They found out that it wasn't good at all.

Moses   Right! You can think about that while I'm gone. Thanks to you, I've got to do all that writing again.

Narrator   And with that, Moses set off back up the mountain. Simon didn't say anything, for a very long time. That was partly because he was so ashamed, but it was mainly because his throat was sore.

The Donkey's Tale

Based on Numbers 22-24

Narrator I'm going to tell you a story, but you mustn't let on that I told you because we donkeys aren't supposed to know things. It's great, being a donkey. Humans talk about all kinds of stuff in front of us and think it doesn't matter. If you've got any secrets, don't mention them in front of donkeys, because we've got long ears.

Anyway, I used to work for a man called Balaam. I was standing outside the window one day when I saw some important visitors coming. I can tell the king's servants a mile off – all posh clothes and no intellect.

1st Servant The king needs your help, Balaam. The Israelite army look as though they're going to invade.

2nd Servant You've got to put a curse on them and stop them.

Balaam I don't believe God wants me to do that. Go away.

Narrator Then some more arrived: even higher officials than the last lot – posher clothes and even less intelligence.

3rd Servant Can't you just come and say what the king wants?

4th Servant Just keep the old so-and-so happy.

Narrator Well, eventually – for the sake of peace and quiet – he decided to go with them. Now I could have told him that this was a bad idea, but he wouldn't have listened. Humans have small ears and big mouths, whereas donkeys' ears are bigger than our mouths which is the right way round. I knew we were heading for trouble, and sure enough, we hadn't got very far when we hit a road block. And I don't mean any old road block. None of your silly poles across the road; this was a shining, ten foot angel. Of course, I did the sensible thing – I turned off into a field. Balaam went mad!

- he *jerked on the reins*
- he *used his whip*
- he *waved his fists in the air*

Balaam   You stupid donkey! Get back on the road!

Narrator   Now, Balaam's eyes are even smaller than his ears, and he couldn't see a ten-foot, digitally illuminated angel when it was right in front of him. I thought about telling him to look, but humans get jealous of animals talking. Then when I moved, so did the angel, and Balaam's foot got scraped against the wall.

Balaam   Ow! That hurt! You stupid animal!

Narrator   That's humans for you. They can drive nails into our feet, to fix shoes on, but if we so much as step on theirs they yell and shout fit to bust! Next time I saw the angel, I sat down. Balaam started hitting me and kicking me. Like it or not, he was going to hear me talk. 'Are you potty?' I said. 'All these years I've been a good donkey to you – d'you think I'd do this for no reason?' Then he got it from the angel as well.

Angel   What d'you mean by hurting a poor dumb animal?

Narrator   Hey! who are you calling dumb?

Angel   But for your donkey, you'd be dead by now.

Balaam   I'm really sorry – honestly. I won't do it again.

Narrator   I'll believe that when I see it!

Angel   Carry on with your journey, but just be careful only to tell the king the truth – even if he doesn't like it.

Narrator   Things got a bit silly after that. The king refused to pay, and Balaam moaned all the way home.

Balaam   All this way, and he refused to pay me just because I didn't say what he wanted. What do you think of that?

Narrator   Who? Me? Oh no. I know which side my bread's buttered. I kept quiet. And kept walking.

All I Want is a Baby

Based on 1 Samuel 1:1-20

Narrator   Once there lived a man called Elkanah, who had two wives. Men were allowed to do that, in those days, but no-one had heard of women's liberation, so women could only have one husband – and often they had to share him. One of Elkanah's wives was called Hannah, and the other was called Pennina, which is a very nice name but she wasn't a very nice person. She was cruel to Hannah.

- she used to *point at her*
- and *stick out her tongue*
- and *make nasty faces*

Pennina   You've got no children. You're useless – can't even do a simple thing like that.

Narrator   Elkanah didn't help, either. He always gave lots more presents to Pennina than to Hannah.

Elkanah   It's not that I love her more than you. She needs more than you do, with all those children of hers.

Narrator   Now wasn't that a clever thing to say! Whenever Elkanah opened his mouth he put his foot in it.

Elkanah   Why do you want children, when you've got me?

Narrator   That hadn't come out quite the way Elkanah meant it to, but Hannah was too angry to notice.

Hannah   Just like a man, to think he's all a woman needs!

Narrator   She got up and ran out of the house to the place of worship. She was really upset and needed somewhere quiet to think and pray. She didn't pray out loud, but just whispered the words.

Hannah   Please, God, if you let me have a child, I promise I'll nurse him well, and then as soon as he can eat ordinary food I'll give him to you.

Narrator	Hannah didn't notice Eli, an old priest, watching her.
Eli	*(Aside)* Oh dear! Another drunk. They think they can come in here to shelter from the rain, and they always end up embarrassing me. *(To Hannah)* I think you'd better leave. You come in here, getting in the way, annoying the paying – I mean praying public.
Hannah	Oh no, sir, I'm not drunk, just terribly unhappy.
Narrator	With that, Hannah burst into tears. Underneath all his priestly dignity, Eli actually had a fairly soft heart. He put his arm around Hannah and tried to comfort her.
Eli	I'm sorry. Do you want to talk about it?
Narrator	Hannah told him the whole story. Eli was very angry.
Eli	Someone ought to give that Pennina woman a good talking to!
Hannah	Oh, no, please don't do that. She's not a bad person, really – and I do have to live with her afterwards, you know. Don't worry – I've said my prayer, and now I'll have to leave it to God.
Eli	Well, you may be right. Off you go home, and try not to worry. I've been working for God for quite a long time, and he hasn't let me down yet.
Narrator	Pennina carried on being nasty to Hannah
Pennina	You're putting on weight. Elkanah won't like that. And it's not as if you've got any excuse, is it? I've still got my figure even after having *all those children*.
Narrator	Hannah just smiled mysteriously. A few months later she had her baby. It was a beautiful little boy, and she called him Samuel. Elkanah was over the moon.
Elkanah	He's going to be a really great camel driver.
Hannah	No, he's not. I promised him to God, and as soon as he can feed for himself, I'm going to take him to the priest.

Appearances Can Be Deceptive

Based on 1 Samuel 16:1-13

Narrator	Long ago, God had a job for Samuel the prophet.
God	Samuel, I want you to go and see Jesse at Bethlehem and anoint one of his sons as king.
Samuel	Bethlehem? Nothing important happens in Bethlehem.
God	My Word! You ain't seen nothin' yet!
Samuel	Pardon?
God	That's my favourite quotation, but it's after your time.
Samuel	Can we just get back to this Bethlehem thing?
God	Just go – I'll tell you which one to anoint.
Narrator	So Samuel turned up at Jesse's house one afternoon.
Jesse	Hello, hello, hello, It's good old Sam the prophet man! Have you come with some message of doom?
Samuel	Look Jesse, I just say what God's given me to say, so if you want to moan at anybody, you'd better talk to him.
Jesse	Silly bloke – can't take a joke!
Narrator	The trouble was that Jesse fancied himself as a bit of a poet – why, no-one could understand – although it was said that one of his sons was a bit of a song writer.

- Samuel *shook his head*
- and he *shrugged his shoulders*
- and he *spread his hands*

Samuel	Just send for your family and we'll get started.
Jesse	All right, Sammy, keep your wig on; how'd I know there's something big on?

Narrator	Samuel was really pleased when the first son arrived.
God	Don't go by his appearance. I look at the heart.
Samuel	Oh, his heart'll be fine – healthy looking chap.
God	Don't get clever with me. You know what I mean.
Narrator	The next one to arrive was Abinadab
Jesse	This is my son – another one.
Samuel	*(Aside)* I've got to get out of here! Where's my oil?
God	Not so fast, sonny! This is not the one.
Jesse	This one is Shammah – takes after his mamma.
Narrator	How long was this going to go on for! Altogether, Jesse presented seven sons to Samuel.
Samuel	Have you got any more?
Jesse	Yes, there's another – he's their baby brother. He's not like the rest – you've looked at the best. I let him earn his keep by caring for the sheep. Here he is.
David	Hello, I'm David.
Samuel	Thank the Lord! He's not a jumped up amateur poet!
Narrator	David was young – and didn't look at all like a king.
God	That's the one! Don't just sit there, get the oil out.
Narrator	Samuel poured some oil over David's head.
Samuel	Well, that's it, Jesse. Don't tell Saul what I've done, or I'll be on the run. Oh, no! I've got to get out of here!
Narrator	With that, Samuel set off away from Jesse's farm.
Samuel	There's one thing about David – he doesn't make up poetry. I wonder which one of them does.

Choose Your Weapons
Based on 1 Samuel 25:1-35

Narrator After David had killed Goliath, he soon became more popular than the king. King Saul was very jealous of him, and tried to kill him. David took a few friends – well, rather a lot actually – and went to live out in the fields and caves, hiding from Saul. One day they were running short of food.

David I know, I'll ask Nabal for help. He owes us a favour or two for driving off those wolves that were after his sheep. I'm sure he'll spare us a little food.

Narrator Now the name 'Nabal' meant 'grumpy', and he was! Nabal didn't see why he should help David out, and he said so to his wife – who was really much too nice to be married to an old grouch like Nabal.

Nabal He's got a cheek, hasn't he, Abigail? Why can't these fugitives earn their own keep, and not keep sponging off decent people?

Abigail Oh, don't be unfair. David and his men have been really helpful. They get on terribly well with our farm workers, you know.

Nabal Shut up, woman! This is men's talk!

Narrator Nabal sent David's men back with a great big 'No!' (Actually, he used a few more words as well, but you won't hear those from me.) David was hopping mad!

David That jumped up little toad! I'll make him wish he hadn't said that – in fact I'll make him wish he hadn't been born! I want four hundred volunteers to go and teach him a lesson. The rest of you can stay and guard the camp.

Narrator Meanwhile, Abigail was very angry with Nabal.

- she *scowled*
- she *shook her fist*
- and then she *wagged her finger*

Abigail   You stupid, pigheaded, half-witted moron! All the time David and his men have been around, have you ever lost a single sheep? No. Have you ever had one tiny complaint? No. But I'll tell you what you have had, you long-eared son of a crossbred donkey: you've had complete security, that's what you've had. No one would dare rob you while David's men are here. And the first time he asks you for anything, what do you do? Just saying 'No' isn't enough for you – you have to insult him, wind him up, give him reason to hate you. And now, hundreds of very angry freedom fighters are going to show you what a stupid pig you are! Sorry – that's unfair – our pigs are relatively intelligent.

Narrator   Nabal sulked – because that's what his name said. Abigail saddled up a donkey – not Nabal, another one – and went out to meet David taking lots of food and other presents as a peace offering. Soon, she met him and sure enough, he was very angry.

Abigail   I'm sorry about my husband; he really lives down to his name, that one! Look, I've brought you lots of food and drink, and I want you to know how grateful I am for the way you've looked after my shepherds. You will forgive me, won't you?

Narrator   Now if there were two things David liked they were power and women, and here was a beautiful woman making him feel powerful. So of course David fell for it straight away.

David   Thank God you came to meet me today! It would have been terrible if we'd done anything to upset you – even though that husband of yours certainly deserves it.

Abigail   Oh he does, my Lord, he does! But I'd be so unhappy if you were angry.

David   I'm not angry any more. Thanks to you, we managed to settle this without using weapons.

Abigail   Without weapons? I'm not so sure about that.

Whose Baby?

1 Kings 3:16-28

Narrator Becky and Sally were both expecting babies. They were flatmates, but they hated one another.

Becky I bet mine will be better looking than yours.

Sally Mine will be brainier; you've always been stupid.

Narrator See what I mean? They couldn't be nice to one another even if their lives depended on it. Becky's baby was born first. It was a beautiful little boy.

Sally Ugh! He's all red and wrinkled – what an ugly child!

Becky All children are like that to start with, but the wrinkles go after a few days. Why didn't yours?

Narrator Sally's baby was born a few days later, and he was lovely – but Becky and Sally still couldn't be friends.

Becky Of course, my baby has nicer eyes than yours.

Sally Mine's ever so good you know – he hardly ever cries.

Narrator One morning, Becky woke up and had a terrible shock. Her baby was very pale, and very cold, and he wasn't breathing. He was dead. Becky cried.

- she *picked the baby up*
- she *rocked him in her arms*
- she *hugged him close*

Sally Hey, I'm trying to sleep. Beautiful women like me need their sleep – it makes no difference to you.

Narrator Becky looked a little closer and realised it wasn't her baby. She rushed over to Sally's crib and there, sure enough, was her child alive and well.

Becky You give me back my baby!

Sally   You're mad! Anyone can see that that's my baby.

Narrator   There was only one thing for it. They would have to get the law on it. King Solomon was just finishing his breakfast when he heard the commotion outside.

Solomon   Really! Can't a royal person even have his breakfast in peace? Be quiet, or I'll have you both locked up until you calm down. Now what's it all about? You first.

Becky   We both had babies and when I woke up this morning mine was dead. Then I realised that Prune-face here –

Sally   Don't you call me Prune-face, Banana-legs!

Solomon   One more word from you and I'll lock you up. Now, Becky, just tell me the story without any silly insults.

Becky   She swapped them. The live baby's mine.

Solomon   Your turn, Sally.

Sally   She's lying. He's my baby.

Solomon   Give me the baby I'm going to cut him in two and you can have half each.

Becky   You can't cut my baby in half!

Sally   Sounds fair to me – give us half each.

Narrator   The servant put the baby on a table, and another took the sword. He lifted it up, high above the baby and waited for the king's command to cut the child in two.

Becky   Give him to her! Give him to her. I'd rather give him away than have him killed.

Solomon   I can tell you're his mother, Becky. When you really love someone, you'd rather let them go than have them hurt. I wouldn't really have hurt him, of course.

Narrator   That was one reason why everybody said that Solomon was a very wise king indeed.

Corruption in High Places

Based on 1 Kings 21:1-25

Narrator King Ahab lived in a wonderful palace with a big garden, and he was married to Jezebel, who was a really horrible person. One day, Jezebel saw their neighbour Naboth (try saying *that* before you put your teeth in!) weeding in his vineyard.

Jezebel Why should an unimportant person have a beautiful vineyard? You should have that land, Ahab.

Ahab That land has been in Naboth's family for generations and it's against the law for him to sell it.

Jezebel What's the law got to do with it? ? You're the king, aren't you! You can have anything you want.

Narrator So next morning Ahab went to see Naboth.

Ahab I've decided that I'm going to have this land.

Naboth Come again?

Ahab This land. I want it.

Naboth Well, tha can't 'ave it!

Ahab I don't think I understand.

Narrator Naboth was beginning to get angry.

- he *stuck his spade in the ground*
- then he *scratched his head*
- then he *poked his finger in Ahab's ribs*

Naboth Oh, is that reet? Well, let me mek it clear for thee. This land belongs to me. Tha can't 'ave it! And I'll tell thee summat else: there's bin a lot o' snails round 'ere lately, so tell that woman o' yourn to quit chuckin' 'em ower t' fence.

Narrator Ahab went home, lay on his bed and sulked.

Narrator Jezebel decided to help. She bribed some bad people to tell lies about Naboth and say that he'd committed a terrible crime.

Naboth What, me? I never did nowt o' t' sort. It's that Jezebel that's be'ind this – well she'll not get me vineyard this road.

Narrator But it was useless. Naboth was sentenced to death, and executed. Meanwhile, Elijah the prophet was just settling down to a date cookie and a cup of pineapple juice when he heard God speaking.

God Elijah, do try to eat and drink more quietly when I'm talking to you.

Elijah Sorry, God, I didn't know you were there.

God Oh don't be tiresome! How many times must I tell you, I'm always here – I just don't talk as much as some people I could mention, that's all.

Elijah I'm listening. What can I do for you?

God Well, I hope your ears are less full than your mouth is; I want you to listen very carefully. It's about the king.

Elijah Oh, no! Not the king What's he been up to now?

God He's stolen Naboth's vineyard.

Elijah I'll go and tell him to give it back.

God Why don't you let your ears do the work for a change, then your mouth can concentrate on eating? Naboth's dead.

Elijah *(Angrily)* You wait until I get my hands on them!

God Really, Elijah! That's a waste of good cookie crumbs – you know the birds round here only eat wholemeal. Look, just go and tell those two they're not going to get away with it.

Narrator Elijah swallowed his cookie as fast as he could, drank his pineapple juice and set off for the palace. I won't tell you the details of what he said to Ahab and Jezebel, because I don't want to put you off your Sunday lunch, but let's just say that by the time he'd finished with them, Ahab and Jezebel hated him even more than they had before!

Elijah's Last Journeys

Based on 2 Kings 2:1-15

Narrator	Elijah, who was the chief prophet, was training Elisha. Elijah was often restless, but on this particular day he really seemed to have sand in his underwear!
Elijah	I'm going to Bethel. You stay here and have a rest.
Elisha	And miss the action? Not likely! I'm coming with you.
Narrator	When they arrived, they were met by the Bethel branch of the Prophets' Commission (known as the PC, but who knew nothing at all about computers).
1st Prophet	Do you know God's going to take Elijah away, today?
Elisha	Yes, but don't tell him. Gosh, can that man walk! I've got blisters where I didn't even know I'd got skin!
Elijah	Look, you rest here. I'm going to go to Jericho.
Elisha	Why? Nothing ever happens in Jericho. Ever since Joshua's jam session, no-one's dared throw a party in case something falls down. Oh, all right – I'm coming.
Narrator	Elijah didn't seem at all tired but went striding ahead. In Jericho, they found another reception committee; this time from the Prophets' Commission, Department Of Soothsaying (otherwise known as PC. DOS, but they didn't know anything about computers, either).
2nd Prophet	Sooth! Sooth!
Elisha	*(Impatiently)* What d'you mean, 'Sooth'?
2nd Prophet	Sorry, Guv, but I've got to say 'Sooth' because I'm a 'Sooth' sayer. Your boss is going away today.
Elisha	Well, don't go yelling 'Sooth' in his ear – or else.
Narrator	The soothsayer looked hurt.

- he *raised his eyebrows*
- he *scratched his head*
- then he *rubbed his nose*

2nd Prophet	Well! I've had my nose bitten off a few times, but that's what I call a mega bite!
Elijah	I'm going to Jordan, Elisha. You wait here.
Elisha	Not on your life! I'm coming, so I can soak these feet!
Narrator	So they went. This time the reception committee was from the Prophets' Bureau (otherwise known as the PBs, who didn't even believe in computers).
3rd Prophet	Did you know...
Elisha	Oh, don't you start as well! Oh, my feet!
3rd Prophet	Sorry, I'm sure!
Elijah	Sorry about all the walking, but we're about there now.
Narrator	Elijah hit the water with his cloak. There, to Elisha's amazement, the water moved aside and left a dry path.
Elijah	Come on, or you'll miss the big moment. Is there anything I can do for you before I go?
Elisha	A double portion of whatever it is that you've got.
Elijah	I'll tell you what. If you see me taken away, then you'll get it. So stick with me, kid – I'm going places.
Narrator	Suddenly, a horse and chariot which seemed to be made of fire came rushing through between them and carried Elijah off. Elisha watched and saw Elijah's cloak coming down to land at his feet. Elisha became a great prophet, and the PCs, the PC. DOS and PBs all said how like Elijah he was – even though none of them knew anything at all about computers.

Elisha's Penthouse Suite

Based on 2 Kings 4:8-17

Narrator   Deborah was an important woman who lived in Shunem. One day she saw a man walking past who looked as though he could do with a rest and a good meal.

Deborah   Hello, you're a stranger round here, aren't you?

Elisha   Yes; my name's Elisha. This is my first visit here.

Deborah   Would you like to come in and have some food?

Elisha   Well, it's very kind of you, but I wouldn't want to be any trouble, and you must have important things to do.

Deborah   Nonsense! I bet you've got some wonderful tales to tell from your travels.

Elisha   I've certainly seen a thing or two. There was that time my best friend got carried away by some flying horses.

Deborah   Now that I really must hear! Come on in.

Narrator   While Elisha was there, Deborah's husband, Bart, came in. He and Elisha got on like a house on fire, and Elisha often visited them after that.

Deborah   You know, Bart, I think Elisha might be a prophet.

Bart   You could be right.

Deborah   I think we ought to build a spare room for him.

Bart   Well, I don't know. We haven't much space.

Narrator   Deborah went and sat outside to think quietly. It *should* have been very peaceful in the garden.

Neighbour   Hello, Deborah, having a nice rest?

Deborah   No, but I'd like to.

Narrator   It was no good, though. Every time anyone walked past, they called out and disturbed her. So to get a bit of peace, she went and got a ladder and climbed up onto the roof. Peace at last – then she had an idea!

Deborah   That's it! Why not build a room for Elisha up here?'

Narrator   Deborah was so excited she forgot about sunbathing rushed off to find Bart, who had gone to market.

Deborah   You'll never believe it – I was just lying on the roof . . .

Bart   You were what?

Deborah   Lying on the roof. Doesn't everybody?

Narrator   Bart liked Deborah's idea and called in a builder.

- the builder *drew some plans*
- and *built some walls*
- and *hammered in some nails*

And soon Elisha had a lovely little room on the roof.

Elisha   I don't know how to thank you.

Deborah   No need. We love having you to stay.

Elisha   There must be something I can do. Perhaps I'll put a good word in for you with the king.

Deborah   Don't be silly! I know him like my own brother. The only thing we want, nobody can give us. Unless you're hiding a spare child in your luggage, just forget it. We love having you here and you don't have to repay us.

Elisha   Ah! So that's what you want. Well, by this time next year, you will have a lovely little baby boy in your arms. You've got God's word for that.

Narrator   And Elisha was absolutely right. But that's another story.

Life's Like That!

Based on 2 Kings 4:18-37

Narrator	Deborah, the Shunemite woman who was a friend of Elisha, was really worried about her husband, Bart. He seemed to be very bad-tempered and unreasonable, and was most unkind about her cooking. But Bart saw things differently, and said so to their neighbour.
Bart	I don't know what's got into her, Luke! Last week, the only food she would cook was figs and onions.
Luke	Figs and onions! You're having me on!
Bart	Would I joke about something as serious as my dinner? Before that, it was stewed oranges in camel meat stock. My stomach's having an identity crisis!
Narrator	Luke thought he had the answer.

- he *scratched his head*
- and he *stroked his beard*
- and he *frowned very wisely*

Luke	She's having some sort of stress-related breakdown.
Bart	Some sort of what?
Luke	Oh, it's very technical. You wouldn't understand – I don't think we'll really understand it for thousands of years yet, but that's what she's having all right.
Narrator	Bart didn't like to ask any more questions, since Luke was now looking very knowledgeable and superior. Just then, though, they heard the sound of shrieking, uncontrollable, hysterical laughter.
Luke	Terribly sorry, old man. Sounds like a serious case.
Bart	That's coming from *your* house. It's *your* wife.
Narrator	Bart was right. Just inside the kitchen window was Luke's wife, Sandy, doubled up, with tears streaming

down her face, and laughing fit to bust!

Sandy   You silly, pompous men! Deborah's pregnant!

Luke   Don't be silly, Sandy! What would you know about it?

Sandy   Well, I've been there myself five times, which is five times more than both of you put together.

Narrator   Poor Luke felt nearly as silly as he looked – but it would have been impossible to have felt that silly!

Bart   What a relief! So we aren't falling out of love, after all! Elisha promised us a child, and we're having one!

Narrator   Soon, they had a lovely little boy whom they named Tom. He grew very strong and healthy for a few years, but then for no apparent reason he died. Deborah was beside herself with grief and anger, and went to find Elisha.

Deborah   Why did you do this? We'd got used to not having a child. Why did your God give us one, just to make us unhappy by taking him away?

Elisha   Let's go to your house!

Narrator   They hurried off, and when they arrived Elisha went up to his room and found Tom's body on his bed. As he prayed, and hugged Tom, a wonderful thing happened. Tom's body started to get warm again, and soon his eyes opened. He really was alive!

Elisha   Deborah, Bart, you can come in now – he's fine.

Deborah   This is wonderful! How can we ever thank you?

Elisha   Don't thank me. It's God that's done this. He doesn't break his word. And he doesn't play around with people's feelings, either. Oh, and by the way, Bart: if you don't like Deborah's cooking, why not lend a hand yourself occasionally?

Keep It Simple
Based on 2 Kings 5:1-14

Narrator Naaman lived in the country of Aram, and was a commander in the king's army. He was often sent by the king of Aram to raid Israel and bring back treasure. The king wasn't really such a bad man; kings just thought they could do that kind of thing in those days, and a lot of rulers and politicians still haven't learnt any better. Anyway, on one of the raids Naaman brought back a young girl called Anna as a slave for his wife, Jessica.

Anna Now you might have thought that I would hate Naaman and Jessica for that, but I always tried not to. After all, we've all got to live together and hating them would just make me feel even more unhappy. Mind you, I really miss my home and I'd love to go back.

Narrator One day, Anna noticed something very worrying about Naaman, and spoke to Jessica about it.

Anna I hope you won't mind me saying this, my Lady, but the commander doesn't seem very well. That nasty rash is getting worse.

Jessica I know – but none of our doctors can cure it.

Anna I know someone who can, though. Send him to the prophet who lives in Israel, and he'll cure him.

Narrator The king of Aram thought it was certainly worth a try, so he sent Naaman to the king of Israel with a letter saying, 'Please make my army commander better.'

Narrator The king of Israel thought Naaman's king was trying to pick a quarrel with him. How could he make anyone better? He got really frightened.

- he *wrung his hands*
- and he *bit his nails*
- and he *hugged himself*

Narrator	Well, you know how rumours about royal families spread – before long the whole country was talking about it, and wondering if it meant the end of the monarchy. But Naaman should have gone to Elisha.
Elisha	Why do people think only kings and queens have the answers to anything? Send him to me.
Narrator	A bit later, Naaman knocked on Elisha's door.
Elisha	Oh, it's you. Go and take seven dips in the river.
Naaman	Is that it? I didn't come here to be made a fool of.
Narrator	Fortunately, as is often the case, Naaman's servant was actually a lot wiser than he was.
Servant	If he'd asked you to do something difficult you'd have done it, just to show off – so why not do this?
Naaman	I suppose so. Anyway, it's hot and I fancy a swim.
Narrator	So Naaman took off his clothes and jumped in.
Naaman	Ugh! What do they empty into the river around here?
Narrator	But Naaman didn't want to look like a wimp – so he went under seven times, just as he'd been told. Then he got out of the water and started to dry himself.
Naaman	There! Satisfied now?
Servant	Sir! Sir! Your rash has gone!
Naaman	Well, well! So it has. How amazing!
Servant	Very often, the simplest ideas are really the best ones.
Naaman	I think you're right. You're quite a philosopher.
Servant	I've been called some names in my time, but really!

Live Connections
Based on Ezekiel 37:1-14

Narrator Hello, there! My name's Ezekiel, but you can call me Zeek if you like. I'm going to tell you about a really amazing vision that I had. I was in a deep valley with bones scattered all over the place. I tell you, everything was so dry that there weren't even any vultures around. They like their food dead – but not that dead. Anyway, while I was wondering, I heard this voice.

God Hey! Zeek!

Narrator Strange, I wonder who that is. What sort of person would come to a place like this? You'd either have to be mad or be God!

God Hey, you! Human being! Homo Sapiens, or whatever your name is.

Narrator Who, me?

God I don't see anyone else here, do you?

Narrator Er – what can I do for you?

God Not a lot. It's really what I can do for you. Tell me, do you think that these dry bones can live?

Narrator God knows!

God Yes, that's right, I do.

Narrator Oh, I'm very sorry. I didn't recognise your voice.

God No a lot of people don't. Now I'm going to show you something really special. All you have to do is say the words I dictate to you.

Narrator Okay. *(Listens)* Yes . . . Mmmm . . . Sorry, I missed that bit. Look, are you sure that's what you want? Okay, okay – you're the boss.
    Now listen here, you dry bones, God's going to join you all together again. Now all you toe bones have got to join up with foot bones, and you ankle bones look snappy and get hooked onto the other side. That's good!

Now where are all you shin bones? All right – tibs and fibs if you want to be technical – you've got to join on to the anklebones, and pick up a kneecap along the way. Right on! Now, I want thigh bones, and pelvis bones, and I want lots of itsy bitsy back bones, and you all join together in just the right order. Now, give me some rib bones, some shoulder bones, some rib-ticklin' funny bones and where have those arm bones got to? Now some finger bones and, what've I forgotten? Well, would you believe it – what about some skull bones, then? And if you promise not to chatter you can have your jawbones too.

Now, what was the next bit again? *(Listens)*

Oh, yes – that's it. Let's have some muscles and some tendons, and for goodness' sake put some skin on – you look revolting.

Well, that's better – but they're not very lively are they?

God　Well, don't just stand there! Talk to the wind.

Narrator　So I called out to the four winds, and d'you know I'd hardly opened my mouth when there was such a whoosh you've never heard before and suddenly all the bodies started to move.

- they *wiggled their fingers*
- they *shook their hands*
- they *turned their heads*

I couldn't help thinking that there was still something missing, but that was the end of the vision.

God　That's how it's going to be. Where you think there's no hope, I'm going to bring new life. People will be happy again, and they'll know that I love them, and they'll all live together and really enjoy life. By the way, you forgot their clothes. Must I think of everything?

Walking Through Fire for God
Based on Daniel 3:1-28

Narrator This is the story of Shadrach, Meschack and Abed-nego. They actually came from Jerusalem, but they had been taken to Babylon as slaves. The king was kind to them though, and life wasn't bad until he got a little too big for his boots. He made a golden statue, and told everybody to worship it. That may seem a bit daft to you, but just be thankful they didn't have rock stars or footballers in those days or they might have worshipped something *really* silly . . .

King As soon as the music starts, you've all got to lie down and pray. And anyone who doesn't will end up in the fiery furnace.

Narrator Shadrach, Meschack and Abed-nego were among the crowd waiting for the music to start.

Shadrach I don't want to worship that monstrosity.

Meschack Neither do I. It can't be a god.

Abed-nego It's an ugly brute, anyway.

Shadrach Of course, beauty is in the eye of the beholder.

Abed-nego Who wrote that?

Shadrach No one yet, but someone famous will, one day.

Meschack I know! Some mindless hooligan scrawled it on the warthog cage at the zoo. That's where you got it from!

Narrator Just then, the music started. Everyone lay down except Shadrach, Meschack and Abed-nego. The King's Personal Private Secretary, who was very bloodthirsty and quite mad, got really excited.

P. P. S. Ooh, look! They're not bowing down! Ooh, Your Majesty! Can I stoke the fire? Nasty little forriners – think they can come here and do as they like! Please let me stoke the furnace, Your Majesty!

King Do shut up! Hey, you three. Bow down and pray.

Shadrach   What, to that heap of scrap metal? Not likely!

Narrator   The king's Personal Private Secretary got excited.

- he *shovelled coal onto the fire*
- he *fanned the flames*
- and he *clapped his hands in delight*

P. P. S.   Ooh! Listen to that! Put 'em in the fire, Your Majesty! Show 'em whose country this is! That'll teach 'em – I'll bet they do as they're told after that!

Narrator   The king was very tempted to put his Personal Private Secretary on the fire as well, but he didn't.

King   Look, you chaps, you don't have to mean it. Just lie down and move your lips, and that will be enough.

Shadrach   No.

King   Well, would you just kneel, then?

Meschack   Not likely!

King   Just a quick bow? If we all close our eyes?

Abed-nego   Not on your life!

P. P. S.   Go on, your Majesty. Burn 'em! Coming in here, bringing all their relations, eating our food, taking our jobs – put em on the fire, Your Majesty! Put 'em on the fire!

King   Oh, you are a pain! Still, you'd better do it.

Narrator   The P. P. S. put the three men into the furnace, but suddenly he came running back towards the king.

P. P. S.   Your Majesty! They're walking about. And none of them are burning! Tell 'em to burn, Your Majesty – tell 'em to burn!

Narrator   The king had the furnace opened, and Shadrach, Meschack and Abed-nego came out. There wasn't so much as a scorched eyebrow between them.

King   That's it. We're not going to worship gold and silver any more. From now on we'll worship God.

The First Lion Tamer
Based on Daniel 6

Narrator Daniel lived a long time ago in Babylon. Because he was wise and clever, King Darius had made him a very important person. That made some people jealous, because Daniel hadn't been born in Babylon but had come from somewhere else. A nasty man called Ned thought he knew how to get rid of Daniel.

- he *straightened his tie*
- and he *smoothed his hair*
- and he *put on his best smile*

Ned Excuse me, Your Majesty. You're such a great king that I think you should pass a new law, saying that no one may pray except to you.

King Yes, I am a good king aren't I? People praying to me, eh? I like that. But what if they refuse?

Ned Well, I did hear the zoo keeper complaining about the cost of lion food the other day, Your Majesty.

King That sounds like a neat idea. Very well, Ned. From now on, anyone who prays to any god other than me will get fed to the lions.

Narrator Can you see what Ned was up to? He knew that Daniel loved to pray every day, and he also knew that not even the king could change a law once he had made it.

Ned Hey, you – Daniel – What d'you think you're doing?

Daniel I'm fishing for kippers! What does it look like?

Ned Oh no you're not! You can't fool me – you're praying.

Daniel Well, Ned, there's no pulling the wool over your eyes, is there?

Narrator So Ned went to see the king.

Ned   Excuse me, Your Majesty, but I found this man praying. He said he was fishing, but he couldn't fool me – he wasn't wearing his wellies.

King   Oh dear! It's you, Daniel. Now what am I going to do? Didn't you know about the new law?

Daniel   Yes, Your Majesty.

Ned   There you are! No excuse! Time to feed the lions!

Narrator   Poor King Darius had no choice. He had to put Daniel in the lions' den. All night long, he worried – he couldn't get a wink of sleep. Then early in the morning he went to the den. He was certain Daniel would be dead.

Daniel   Good morning, Your Majesty. Did you sleep well?

King   No, I had a – Daniel! What are you doing alive!

Daniel   I suppose you wouldn't believe me, either, if I said I was fishing?

Narrator   The king was so pleased that Daniel was alive that he didn't punish him for being cheeky. Instead, he sent for Ned.

King   I'm a bit worried about the lions, Ned. They seem to be off their food at the moment.

Ned   I suppose you'd better send for the vet.

King   No, I don't think they'd find him very tasty, either. Anyway, I know what the problem is.

Ned   Really, Your Majesty?

King   I think the lions are like you, Ned. They don't like foreigners. Now what we need is some good native food for them, and I know just where I can get some.

Narrator   Poor Ned. The last thing he ever expected was to be eaten by a lion. The *very* last thing, he ever expected . . .

A Camel's Eye View

Based on Matthew 2:1-12

Narrator My name's Constance, and I'm a camel – and before anyone says I've got the hump, let me tell them that that joke isn't funny any more. Or not to a camel of my breeding, anyway. I'm a Bactrian camel, which means I'm straight out of the top drawer of four legged Arabian society, but this story's actually about the people who live in my annexe – Caspar, Balthazar and Melchior, otherwise known as the Three Wise Men. It all began one evening when I was relaxing with my friend Clarissa, chewing at some very tasty fig leaves.

Caspar Melchior! Balthazar! Look!

Balthazar That's some star! What d'you think, Melchior?

Melchior That's the star of a new king. Saddle the camels.

Narrator Well! We trailed across the desert following this star. My dears, it was simply frightful! We had to put up with sandstorms, flies and the most obnoxious little sand lizards who seemed to think they had as much right to be there as we did. Really! Eventually, we seemed to have arrived.

- Melchior *held up his hand*
- then he *peered into the distance*
- and then he *pointed with his finger*

Melchior There's the king's palace.

Narrator That seemed an appropriate place for a quadruped of my breeding. Caspar knocked on the door.

Herod Good evening, I'm King Herod. Can I help you?

Narrator (*Aside*) Hello, hello, hello, he's a wrong 'un or I'm an African Elephant.

Caspar Hello, we're the three wise men.

Herod How wonderful to meet you! I'm Herod the Great – but great what, I can never remember. Do come in –

	d'you take one lump or two?
Narrator	Smarmy character – wouldn't trust him as far as I could throw him. The wise men came out a little later, all excited.
Caspar	Well, who'd have thought it – Bethlehem.
Narrator	Oh, no! Bethlehem, my dears, is one of those dreadful little tourist resorts where the common creatures go. Most of the humans ride *donkeys* – and some even walk! Would you believe it?
Melchior	What a nice man Herod is – we must remember to tell him where the new king is after we've found him.
Balthazar	Yes, then he can pay his respects, as well.
Narrator	Pay his respects? If they believe that, then they'll believe anything!
Melchior	The star's stopped. This is the place
Narrator	Well, I always had my doubts about astrology. It was a horrid, smelly, draughty little hovel of a stable. And there, inside, was a baby and – my dears, you'll never guess – it was lying in a feeding trough, with the most disreputable ox I have ever seen breathing all over it. Then in went the three wise men – 'wise'? – I like that! And they offered their presents.
Melchior	I've brought the king some gold.
Caspar	And I've got some frankincense
Balthazar	Here's some lovely myrrh
Narrator	Ugh! Nasty, smelly stuff! And to think that all the way along I've been blaming Clarissa's feet! Anyway, next morning we got ready to leave.
Caspar	Let's give the palace a miss. An angel told me that Herod's not to be trusted.
Narrator	Well, I could have told him that! Anyway, we went home by a different way – and a longer one – and Clarissa's feet haven't been right since.

Trials and Temptations

Based on Matthew 4:1-11

Narrator Jesus was sure God had a very special job for him, but wasn't clear exactly what he should do.

Jesus I think I'll get away somewhere quiet for a bit, Mother.

Mary How long will you be gone?

Jesus You never know with God – don't wait up.

Narrator Jesus stayed away for well over a month. One day, he heard a cunning, deceitful little voice.

Devil I bet you're hungry. Why not have something to eat?

Jesus I'm trying to concentrate. Anyway, there isn't anything.

Devil Oh, come on! You know better than that! Why not make bread out of these stones? Might I recommend a nice fig and walnut sandwich?

Jesus That's not what I'm here for. The Bible says that we don't only live by bread, but by the word of God.

Devil Oh, if you're going to quote the Bible . . . Look, you've got to get people's attention. How will you do that?

Jesus That is exactly what I'm trying to work out. So why not just run away and play, and let me get on with it?

Devil Well, since you're good at quoting the Bible, doesn't it say that God won't let you get hurt? Why not jump off the temple tower? Now there's a gimmick!

Jesus I'm not here to do stunts.

Devil *(Persuasively)* Not stunts: *Miracles.*

Jesus Stunts. Miracles are to help people. Stunts are to show off. And Scripture says we shouldn't test God out.

Devil Oh, that! It all depends what you mean by 'test', doesn't it? Anyway, you should listen to me. I can be good for you. Why don't you take a look around?

Jesus   I don't need to. The answer's not out there; it's in me.

Devil   Oh, don't be such a stuffed toga! Live a little! Dream a little!

Narrator   Jesus looked around and could hardly believe his eyes!

- he *looked to the left*
- he *looked to the right*
- and he *blinked in amazement!*

He could see all the wonderful things in the world: tall buildings and towers, with onion-shaped roofs; huge triangular buildings like synthetic mountains; wonderful jungles with beautiful wild animals and birds; it was like being up in a space shuttle with a telescope – except no one had invented telescopes in those days.

Devil   I can give it all to you if you just do things my way. And how about you putting in a good word for me? There's so much prejudice out there, and devils are having a hard time at present. Do we have a deal?

Jesus   All that isn't yours to give. I'm sticking with God, so why don't you just find a quiet hole to crawl into?

Narrator   There was a long silence, and when the voice came again, it sounded different – weak, and desperate.

Devil   Are you sure you wouldn't like a sandwich? Call it a free sample. No obligation.

Jesus   I've already said no! So go on, push off!

Devil   (*Sulkily*) All right, but I'll be back. See you around.

Narrator   As Jesus set off for home, he knew he'd chosen the harder way. He also knew that that horrible little voice would be back, but he wasn't too worried about it. After all, he'd turned down its best offer once, and he could do it again.

Jesus Makes Matthew Rich

Based on Matthew 9:9-13

Narrator	When the Romans invaded Israel, most of the Israelites were very angry about it – but not Matthew. He could make a profit out of anything – including an invasion. One day the Roman governor sent for him
Governor	How would you like to collect taxes for me?'
Matthew	That depends. What's in it for me?
Governor	Whatever you like. I don't care how much you cheat these people, just as long as you get the taxes in.
Matthew	Sounds good, but I'm not sure. Everyone will hate me.
Governor	Yes, but if you refuse me *I* might hate you.
Matthew	Yes, yes, of course, Your Excellency! It would be an honour to work for the glorious Roman Empire.
Narrator	So, next morning, Matthew was in a new office with a big desk and chair, and with a notice on the outside saying *All Taxes Collected. No credit – No I.O.U.s – No Forged Fivers, Dubious Dollars or Duff Denarii.* Matthew quickly became very rich – but unhappy.
Matthew	It's awful! I haven't any friends any more. People call me names, and write things on my front door, and I can't even pop down the road to buy a pomegranate without a bodyguard.
Narrator	One day, he was having an argument with a taxpayer.
Taxpayer	You're charging too much.
Matthew	Look, Smartie-pants, if you had to do this rotten job—
Taxpayer	Oh, hearts and flowers! Some people would be glad to have a job at all.
Jesus	You having a spot of bother, Matthew?

Narrator Matthew looked up and saw Jesus. He'd always thought Jesus was a useless, woolly minded romantic – spreading silly ideas like there were more important things than money. Suddenly, Matthew sat bolt upright.

Matthew Tell you what, let's just forget the whole thing. Go away. Keep your money. I don't know what you see in the lousy stuff anyway! Nothing but trouble, if you ask me. Here you are, everybody.

- he *handed out money*
- then he started *throwing it around*
- then he *washed his hands*

That's it, Jesus! I've had it with money. Filthy stuff!

Jesus Don't blame the money – we all need a bit of that. Your problem is that you're addicted to it. Now if you were with me, you'd never have the chance to get addicted to anything – there's never enough of it around!

Matthew If you don't mind my saying so, your appearance isn't exactly an advert for simple living, is it?

Jesus Oh, I don't know. No-one writes nasty things on my front door, because I haven't got one – and I don't have trouble with my tailor, either. I'll tell you what I have got, though. I've got friends – I'm never short of a place to stay – and when it comes to money –

Matthew All right! You can start by coming for lunch with me.

Narrator The religious leaders were horrified – and said so.

Pharisee That Jesus fellow mixes with all the wrong people!

Jesus Well, if you're as good as you think you are, you don't need me. Doctors don't do house calls for people who are fit. By the way, Matthew, you do realise that if you resign the Governor will have your head for it?

Matthew He'll have to find me first, and as of right now I haven't got an address.

Don't Be Stingy!

Based on Matthew 13:1-9

Narrator   Jesus wanted to show how generous God is with his love. So he told a story a bit like this one.

It's about Sally, who was a very good farmer – but her neighbour, Jake, didn't approve of her. He would lean on the fence while Sally worked, and make comments.

Jake   You've got to maximise the return on your investment, you know. You ought to target your resources.

Narrator   One day, Sally decided to start growing her own wheat, to make bread. She started getting the land ready for sowing, while Jake looked over the fence.

Jake   Growing some wheat? No money in it these days; the big boys have got it buttoned up. You'll never make it pay. What d'you pay for your seeds? Too much, I'll bet. You've got to keep unit costs in mind, you know.

Narrator   When Sally sowed her seeds, Jake was shocked.

- he *leaned on the fence*
- and he *shook his head*
- and he *stroked his beard*

Jake   You can't just go scattering seeds around like that! Target your resources – how often must I tell you! Look, you've gone and spilt some among those thistles. Hey! Mind the path! Nothing will grow there.

Sally   No, I don't suppose it will.

Jake   Mind the rockery! Really, Sally, you'll never make a proper living as a farmer! Just like a woman!

Narrator   Sally decided to ignore that. She finished off her work and went inside. Jake just stood there, leaning on the fence, and shaking his head in despair. Sally looked out of the window and saw a flock of birds on the path, eating the seeds she had dropped there.

Sally	Well, they've got to eat as well. And if they eat the seed on the path, they're leaving the rest alone.
Narrator	Very soon, wheat started to sprout – in the rockery.
Sally	I won't get too excited about that. There's not enough soil there, so it won't last. Still, I expected that.
Narrator	Sure enough, when the sun got really hot, the wheat was scorched and it died.
Jake	I told her it wouldn't grow. There's a bit sprouting there, in the thistles, but it won't last. You mark my words.
Narrator	He was right. The thistles were very strong and they just choked the new wheat shoots.
Jake	See? You women should really listen to us men. I don't know why your husband doesn't sort you out.
Sally	What, Tom? Tom wouldn't know a cauliflower from a buttercup! He's a fisherman. 'Sort me out'! Oh, what a joke – Tom will love that one!
Narrator	Over the next few months, little green shoots appeared and grew tall. Very soon they were dense and high enough for rabbits and field mice to hide in them. Sally and Tom watched as the colour changed gradually, and eventually they had a wonderful crop of golden wheat waving gently in the wind. As soon as it was ripe, Sally and Tom harvested the corn, while Jake looked over the fence and gave them advice.
Jake	Don't miss any. Make the most of your investment.
Narrator	When the wheat was gathered in, Sally was overjoyed.
Sally	Some of those seeds must have produced thirty, or sixty or even a hundred times as much!
Jake	If you'd been more careful, you'd have had even more.
Sally	If I'd followed your advice, I'd never have risked sowing any seeds at all.

Nancy's Nightmare
Based on Matthew 25:31-end

Narrator It was an ordinary night when Nancy went to bed, but next thing she knew she was in a very strange place.

Nancy I've died. That's what it is. So this must be heaven.

Narrator Nancy had always known she was a good person. She went to church regularly, never used a naughty word, always kept her home clean and saved her money. So Nancy was not surprised to find herself in heaven.

Sheila Hi, Nance! What're you doing here?

Narrator Nancy was horrified; it was Sheila, her neighbour. She hadn't been near a church in forty years – and her house was always untidy. Well it would be: she was never there to clean it – always off helping at the night shelter, or prison visiting. Well, *she* wouldn't be getting in to heaven! Nancy put on her best smile, and waited for a big welcome. God spoke to Sheila first.

God Welcome! Thank you for feeding me when I was hungry and thirsty – and for helping me when I was lost – and d'you remember when I hadn't any clothes and you gave me some? Oh, yes, and of course when I was sick you came to see me – and even when I was in prison.

Sheila Me? I never did those things for you!

God You did them for other people – people who seemed unimportant. And that means you did them for me.

Narrator A door opened and an angel took Sheila through. It sounded as if a really terrific party was going on through there. Fancy having *that* kind of music in heaven!

God Well, Nancy, I hope you don't think you're coming in.

Nancy What? I've been at church every Sunday! I've always been clean and responsible – not like some people!

God   Maybe, but where were you when I was hungry, or thirsty? Why wouldn't you help me when I was lost? And what about that time when I was naked?

Narrator Nancy didn't know what to say. The whole idea of God going around without any clothes on was beyond her! Nice people didn't do that kind of thing!

God   And whenever I've been in hospital, or in prison, I might as well not have existed for all you cared.

Nancy   I – I don't remember any of this. I've never seen you anywhere before – and certainly not in *that* condition!

God   No, but you've seen my people like that, which is just the same, and you've done nothing. No arguments, now! There are no strings you can pull here.

Narrator Suddenly, he was gone. Everything was dark and cold. Nancy felt herself falling, and landed with a bump. Slowly she opened her eyes. She could see grotesque shadows. Ugh! Then she heard a click.

Announcer This is the early morning news from the BBC.

Narrator It had all been a horrible nightmare – and poor Nancy had fallen out of bed! What a relief! Nancy got up and made a cup of tea, and began to think about herself. She didn't seem half such a nice person any more.

Nancy   Perhaps there are more important things than being respectable, and I'm going to start doing them. Let me see: hungry, thirsty, strangers, naked sick, in prison . . . Where on earth do I start! I need some advice.

Narrator
- Nancy *looked in the phone book*
- she *picked up the telephone*
- and she *dialled the number*

Nancy   Hello, Sheila. Could I come to see you sometime?

Narrator And quite a lot of people lived happily ever after.

'Are You a Friend of Jesus?'

Based on Matthew 26:30-39, 51-58, 69-75

Narrator	Peter was a friend of Jesus. He knew he would never let Jesus down. He told him so, as well.
Peter	I'll always be your friend. Even if I have to die for you, I won't ever let you down.
Narrator	One evening, Jesus arranged to celebrate a special meal with his disciples, and afterwards, when they were out walking, he said something very strange.
Jesus	You're all going to break down. You're going to run away and leave me when things go wrong.'
Peter	No, Jesus! We'll never do that. And even if the rest of them do, I won't – even if I have to die.
Jesus	Peter, I know you mean well, but by the time the cock crows you'll have said you don't know me three times.
Peter	Who – me?! Never! I'm no chicken – I'll stick with you.
Narrator	The other disciples all said the same.
Jesus	Well, just stay here, all of you. I'm going over there to pray.
Narrator	It was very late at night, and the disciples were tired. They didn't mean to fall asleep, but fall asleep they did until the noise woke them up. There seemed to be soldiers everywhere. Jesus was standing calmly waiting for the guards to arrest him, and Peter decided to do something.

- he *drew his sword*
- and he *lifted it up*
- and he *brought it down hard*

Narrator	And one of the gang found his ear had been cut off. Jesus stepped forward in front of Peter.

Jesus	No, that's not right. Let me handle this my own way.
Narrator	Then Jesus reached out and healed the man's ear. Peter couldn't believe it! All that stuff about loving your enemies was fine in theory, but Jesus should have known it was no way to handle this!
Peter	Take cover, everybody!
Narrator	Peter dived into the bushes, closely followed by all Jesus' other friends. They looked round just in time to see Jesus being arrested. They were very frightened, and ran off, but Peter crouched low in the shadows and followed to the High Priest's house where Jesus was put on trial. Peter sneaked in and warmed his hands by the fire while he listened to what was going on. People were telling dreadful lies about Jesus, and then one of the servants spotted Peter.
1st Servant	Hey you! You're one of his friends, aren't you!
Peter	Who? Me? I don't know what you're talking about.
2nd Servant	Yes you are. I've seen you with him.
Peter	Not me! Never seen him before in my life!
3rd Servant	Yes, you're one of them – you've got a northern accent. You northerners are all dangerous revolutionaries.
Peter	Honestly, as God's my judge, I don't know him.
Narrator	It was then that the cock crowed: the most dreadful sound that Peter had ever heard, because he remembered what Jesus had said. Peter pushed his way outside, where, he collapsed in a heap on the ground and cried and cried and cried!
Peter	I learnt a lot from that. I learnt that I wasn't as strong as I thought. I learnt that it's best not to make rash promises unless I really know I can keep them. And a little while later, I learnt something really wonderful. I learnt that even when people let Jesus down as badly as that, we can still be forgiven and still be Jesus' friends.

The Voice in the Wilderness
Based on Mark 1:1-11

Narrator   There was once a priest called Zechariah, who was married to Elizabeth. They had a son, John, who was turning out to be a real embarrassment to them.

Elizabeth   I'm fed up with you looking scruffy. Tidy yourself up!

John   There are more important things than looks, Mother.

Zechariah   Right! No pocket money for a week, for being cheeky.

John   There are more important things than money, as well.

Elizabeth   That does it! Off to bed with you – and no supper! What will the neighbours say?

John   What will the *congregation* say?

Narrator   As John grew up, he didn't get any better. He picked up some very strange ideas, and when he preached his father cringed in embarrassment.

John   Repent your sins! Prepare to meet your God!

Narrator   The trouble was, lots of people seemed to believe John, and he spent days at a time at the river Jordan baptising people. One day, some of Zechariah's friends, who were also priests, offered to help.

Levi   We'll talk to him. He'll listen to us.

Zechariah   Thank you, Levi. That's good of you.

Narrator   So they put on their best robes and went to see John.

John   Ooh, you snakes! You think you're so special, but God could make better priests out of stones!

Levi   Just who do you think you are? Elijah or somebody? I bet you think you're a great prophet come back to life.

John   All I am is a voice in the wilderness warning you of someone greater who is on his way. I'm not good enough even to help him take off his shoes.

Narrator	Levi didn't get the chance to answer, because John was suddenly surrounded by people wanting to know what to do to be better people.
John	Share everything, and treat poor people fairly. You tax collectors should charge people a fair tax, and don't cheat. And soldiers, don't abuse your power.
Jesus	And what about me? Will you baptise me?
John	(*Amazed*) I can't baptise you, Jesus – you're good – it's you who should baptise me.
Narrator	Levi and his friends were horrified! How could John call this common carpenter good, after all he'd said about them? But while they were watching, Jesus went into the water with John to be baptised.

- when he came out, he *wiped his eyes*
- *brushed back his hair*
- and *dried himself on a towel*

Then an amazing thing happened. A dove seemed to be hovering over Jesus – but everyone knows that doves can't hover. Then there was a voice – not quite like anything they had heard before. Was it a man? Was it a woman? Was it a child? It was very mysterious.

God	This is my son, whom I love very much.
Narrator	Levi couldn't help being puzzled and a little worried as he and his friends went away to see John's parents.
Zechariah	Well, what happened? Did he listen to you?
Elizabeth	Had he combed his hair recently?
Levi	I'm afraid it's bad news. He's obviously not going to listen to us, and he's got some really strange friends. I don't think we've heard the last of them by a long way.

Perfectly Willing to Learn

Based on Mark 7:24-30

Narrator	Lydia was a very nice person; she was also angry about always being treated differently from other people because she came from another country. Andy, one of her neighbours, tried to give her a little advice.
Andy	You should try to be more like us. After all, 'When in Rome, do as the Romans do'.
Lydia	You hypocrite! When you go abroad you behave just the same as you do at home – so why shouldn't I?
Andy	I'm not prejudiced, you know. Some of my best friends are foreigners. I just think you should all be like us.
Lydia	I think you'd better go, before I'm rude to you.
Narrator	Lydia was from Syria, and the Syrians all lived in the same area. If they went to live anywhere else, people were rude to them, and got up petitions about them because they thought their houses might be worth less money if 'Syroes' lived nearby. So they all lived close together in their own communities, and were accused of being unfriendly and not mixing! They couldn't win. Lydia had a daughter, whose name was Ria. Ria was a lovely little girl, just nine years of age, but she was very unhappy.
Ria	I hate being bullied! They call me a 'Syro brat'.
Lydia	Then don't play with them.
Ria	Then they call me a 'stuck up little Syro' – I can't win.
Narrator	One day, Lydia heard that the famous healer, Jesus, was in the area. Now of course, Ria wasn't actually sick – it was the unkind people around them who were sick – but Lydia knew that Ria needed a kind of healing, if she was not to be destroyed by her own anger.
Lydia	Excuse me, Jesus. Sorry to be a nuisance, but –

Narrator	Jesus was tired, and his friends tried to send her away.
Peter	If you're sorry, why are you doing it?
Narrator	Lydia was angry.

- she *wagged her finger at Peter*
- and she *shook her fist*
- and then she *snapped her fingers*

Lydia	I'm talking to the organ grinder, not his pet monkey.
James	You can't talk to us like that. We're his special friends, you know. He's going to make us important people in his kingdom – our mum's arranging it, isn't she John?
John	Yes, James. *(To Lydia)* So you just watch your manners.
Narrator	By now, Jesus had heard the racket.
Jesus	What do you want?'
Lydia	I just want my daughter healed. She's full of all kinds of anger and resentment – not that I blame her for that – but it's beginning to get to her. Can you help?
Jesus	I'm here for the people of Israel first. It's not right to take food from children and feed it to the dogs.
Lydia	Even the dogs get the scraps that fall from the table.
Jesus	You're a shrewd one! All right – I'm sorry. You've persuaded me. Go on home, and you'll find your daughter in a much better frame of mind.
James	Surely you're not admitting you were wrong, Jesus? Especially to a *foreigner*.
Jesus	There's nothing to be ashamed of in making the odd mistake – only in being too pig headed to admit it. I'm *perfectly* willing to learn.
Narrator	Then the disciples knew that Jesus really was a most extraordinary person.

Speechless With Surprise
Based on Luke 1:5-25

Narrator   Zechariah couldn't believe what was happening to him! It had started just like any ordinary Sabbath day, with him going to lead worship. He had to go right into the 'holy of holies', behind a curtain. No-one could go there unless he was a priest – I say 'he' because only men could become priests, then. As he began to light the incense, Zechariah realised that he wasn't alone in the sanctuary – out of the corner of his eye, he could see a figure standing by his shoulder.

Zechariah   Whoever you are, you'd better go – before God strikes you dead or something.

Gabriel   Oh, I don't think he'll do that. He doesn't often strike angels dead, you know. Gabriel's the name.

Zechariah   Well, I'll go to the foot of our stairs!

Gabriel   Not right now; I want a word with you. God's going to give you and Elizabeth a son. You're going to call him John, and he's going to be a really great man – he's going to prepare the way for the Messiah.

Zechariah   Is that what you've come here for – just to tease an old man? Look, my wife's old. So am I, of course, but we men don't show it as much, do we? Anyway, we're too old to have children and that's it. And if we did have a child, he wouldn't be called John. There've been Zechariahs in my family for generations, and no-one has ever had a common old name like John!

Gabriel   This is me you're talking to – Gabriel – I've taken more messages for God than your entire family's had hot dinners, and no-one – no-one, I tell you – has ever called me a liar before. No, it's no good trying to protest, because you can't talk – so for once you're going to have to listen. It's time you priests learned to do that anyway. As I said, you're going to have a son. You'll call him John, and he'll be a great preacher who will prepare the way for the Messiah. Got it? Oh, sorry, you can't speak can you? Well, that will give your congregation a bit of a break. Toodle-oo!

Narrator Then the archangel had gone, and just as he had said Zechariah was completely unable to speak. Outside, the congregation were getting impatient because he should have started the service, and Zechariah had to try to signal to them that he'd lost his voice.

Worshipper 1 He must have seen a vision.

Worshipper 2 Rubbish! It's that incense that's got to him. I've said it before and I'll say it again, worship should be plain and simple without all that 'high synagogue' nonsense.

Narrator By the time the baby was born, the whole neighbourhood was excited. Everyone was talking about it – well, everyone except Zechariah. The neighbours came round and they all sang hymns to celebrate – well, all except Zechariah.

Neighbour What are you going to call him?

Elizabeth We're going to call him John.

Neighbour Why John? You're supposed to call him after one of Zechariah's family. You can't call him John!

Narrator Zechariah got a bit cross with the neighbours for laughing about it.

- he *picked up a pen*
- and he *dipped it in the ink*
- and he *wrote a note*

The note said, 'His name's John, and that's an end to it.'

Neighbour All right, no need to be stroppy.

Zechariah (*Shouts*) I'm not being stroppy! Hey, I can talk!

Narrator Everyone laughed, and the celebrations began again. They went on well into the night, and this time Zechariah could join in properly.

The Women's Story

Based on Luke 1:26-40

Narrator   This is the story of Mary. She lived a very long time ago in a town called Nazareth. Yes, that's right – *that* Mary. She wasn't very old – perhaps sixteen or thereabouts, but in those days girls got married very young, and people were beginning to talk.

Gossipper 1   What about Mary? She's on the shelf you know – should be married and have a family by now.

Gossipper 2   After all, having babies is what women are for, isn't it? And if she can't get a husband there's no way she can do that.

Narrator   One day, Mary was doing some work around the house. There was a broken chair and she knew that if she waited for her father to mend it then it would never be done, so she went and found some glue.

- she *opened the jar*
- she *dipped in the brush*
- and she *brushed on the glue*

Just then, she heard a voice.

Gabriel   Hello, Mary.

Mary   Hello. Who's that?

Gabriel   I'm the archangel Gabriel.

Mary   Very pleased to meet you, I'm sure. I'm sorry not to look up, but I've just got to the tricky bit. If you want my parents, I'm afraid their both out but they'll be back about six. If you want the Rabbi, he lives just down the road, and –

Gabriel   Mary! Mary! Let me get a word in edgeways. It's you I've come to see. I've been sent to tell you that God's very pleased with you. He thinks you're a really special person.

Mary	Oh, it's nothing really. Anyone can mend a chair if they really want to.
Gabriel	Not that! You're going to have a baby. He's going to be a great ruler and save the world. He'll be known as the Son of God, and he'll rule for ever.
Mary	Me? Have a baby? That's a bit difficult for a single girl, isn't it?'
Gabriel	If God's decided to use you in a special way, why should he need some man to help him?
Mary	Well, it's usual, at least where having babies is concerned.
Gabriel	Nothing's impossible for God. You know your cousin Elizabeth, who's never been able to have a baby?
Mary	Yes. Everyone thinks she's no good because of that.
Gabriel	It's certainly a very unfair world, isn't it? Women seem to get the blame for everything. Anyway, she's going to have a baby as well – she's six months pregnant. So don't you go saying that anything's impossible where God's concerned.
Mary	Well, God's the boss – so it's O.K. by me.
Gabriel	Good! That's what he hoped you'd say.
Narrator	As soon as Gabriel had gone, Mary threw away the chair she was mending and all the bits fell apart again, but she was too excited to bother with mending a silly old chair! After all, any man can do that, but they can't have babies, can they? Mary got her coat and scarf, and then she ran out of the house and all the way to her cousin Elizabeth's place. They were so happy – they hugged one another, and they danced and sang, and were completely overjoyed. God had chosen both women for a special purpose, and no-one could ever look down on either of them any more. It had always been a silly thing to do, anyway – hadn't it!

There's a Baby in My Dinner!

Based on Luke 2:1-20

Narrator Why are human beings so obsessed with numbers? They count everything! You wouldn't find self-respecting donkeys wasting all our time counting things. Life's too short for that. Anyway, the government had the bright idea of counting all the people. Joseph and Mary weren't pleased.

Joseph We've been told we've got to go to Bethlehem.

Mary Whatever for?

Joseph To be counted. We've all got to go back to the town we first came from.

Mary Oh, great! And me about to have a baby!

Narrator I'm not surprised Mary wasn't thrilled. Bethlehem is a wonderful place to come from – but it's a lousy place to *go to*. And now we're here. Mary rode the whole way here on my back. Now that's all very well, but when did you last see a pregnant donkey being given a piggyback by a human? Never. Precisely. It's species discrimination and I intend to make a complaint. But it got worse. I was just settling down in my stable when Mary and Joseph came in with the innkeeper.

Innkeeper I'm sorry, but this is simply all I have available.

Joseph Well it's not good enough.

Mary Oh, do lay off, Joseph. I'm too tired to argue. This will just have to do.

Narrator I tell you, I didn't believe it! I told Joseph right from the start he should have booked, but would he listen? And it got worse. When the baby was born they put it to bed in my dinner! No kidding! Slapped it straight into the manger without so much as a 'by your leave'! Still, I must admit there's something very special about a human baby – they're sweet little things. Naturally, I wanted to have a look, so I wandered over to the manger.

Mary AAAAH! Get that dreadful animal away!

Narrator	She didn't say that when she was using me as a four wheel drive on the way here! Joseph got hold of my collar and started to drag me away. I tell you I'd just about had enough. Maybe I overreacted, I don't know, but I dug my hooves into the earth floor and refused to move an inch.

- Joseph *pulled*
- and he *pulled*
- and he *pulled*

	But I just stood there. Boy, was he mad! Very soon, the innkeeper came to see what the fuss was about.
Innkeeper	Leave this to me. If I put this bucket of hot oats over here . . .
Narrator	Of course, I knew what the game was, but I'd made my point. After all, donkeys are stubborn but we're not stupid. So I walked over to the bucket and pretended not to notice Joseph tying me up. Then, just as I thought we might all get some sleep we had visitors. I ask you – at that time of night!
Shepherd 1	We don't want to be a nuisance.
Narrator	That means they're going to be.
Shepherd 2	We're shepherds, and while we were minding the sheep an angel told us this was a special baby.
Narrator	Oh, that's a good one! I haven't heard that one before. I mean, what shepherd who's any good leaves the sheep in the field at night unprotected? Even if they did, they wouldn't admit it.
Joseph	Oh, please come in. How kind of you!
Narrator	Easily taken in – that's his trouble. But I've got them rumbled. I know salesmen when I see them. You mark my words, before those people leave, Mary and Joseph will have spent money they can't afford on pretty little bootees with lambs all over them – now donkeys I could understand.

(Do you think the donkey's right about the visitors?)

Silly, Snobbish Simon

Based on Luke 7:36-end

Narrator   Simon was a very important person. He was a lawyer and a religious leader.

Simon   Everyone respects me in the town, because I'm friends with all the right people – and none of the wrong ones.

Lydia   What about Jesus? You ought to have him for a friend.

Simon   You must be joking, Lydia! He's an untrained wandering preacher, and he's got some very funny ideas.

Lydia   He's very popular, though, and he might be useful to you one day. Why not invite him round for a meal?

Narrator   Eventually, the day arrived, and so did a lot of Simon's friends. When, Jesus arrived, Simon and Lydia were so busy impressing their guests they didn't even notice that Jesus had arrived until after he and his friends had sat down.

- Jesus *peeled a banana*
- John started *eating the trifle*
- and Peter *drank some wine*

Suddenly, there was a lot of noise from the hallway; it seemed as though there was some sort of fight going on. Someone was trying to gatecrash the party!

Woman   You get out of my way! I want to see Jesus!

Narrator   A woman rushed in, ignored Simon completely and went over to Jesus. She didn't say anything at all. She just sat down by Jesus' feet and cried, and cried and cried. Before very long, Jesus' feet were really wet. The woman used her hair to wipe them dry, and then she opened a jar she'd been carrying and poured out some beautifully perfumed cream which she rubbed into them. By now everyone had stopped eating and was staring at what was going on.

Simon	You know who she is, don't you, Lydia? She's thoroughly immoral – dreadful woman! This proves what I've always said about Jesus. If he were really a holy man he wouldn't let a woman like her touch him – let alone gush over him like that.
Narrator	The only person in the room who didn't seem worried by what was going on was Jesus. Everyone else was terribly embarrassed, but he just sat there and watched what the woman was doing. He wasn't afraid, and he wasn't embarrassed. He knew why she needed to behave like that, and he was quite willing to let her do it.
Jesus	Simon, can I ask you a question?
Simon	If you like, Jesus.
Jesus	Answer me this. There were two people who owed their boss money – one of them just a few pence and the other thousands of pounds – but he told them to forget about it, and not bother to repay it. Now, who do you think would be most grateful?
Simon	Simple! The one who had been forgiven the most.
Jesus	That's right. Now of course you don't think you've got any need for forgiveness, do you? So you don't show much love, either. I walked over dusty roads to get here, and you didn't even have the good manners to give me water so that I could wash – but this woman has washed my feet and dried them on her own hair! You were too busy with your posh friends even to give me a proper welcome – but she's been kissing my feet. Now she's obviously been forgiven – and that's why she's so full of love. But of course, someone who's never even asked to be forgiven (mentioning no names of course) never really learns to love.
Narrator	Simon and Lydia were very careful never to ask Jesus to their house again; in fact they kept him at a safe distance from then on in case he embarrassed them even more.

Poor Ebenezer!

Based on Luke 12:16-21

Narrator Ebenezer was a very careful little boy. All he wanted was to be rich. So he always saved his pocket money.

Ebenezer After all, if you look after the pennies, the pounds will look after themselves.

Narrator He would never lend anything to the other children.

Ebenezer Neither a borrower nor a lender be.

Narrator And he never gave his pocket money to charity.

Ebenezer People should learn to look after themselves.

Narrator Ebenezer never had any friends – but he didn't mind.

Ebenezer Friends are no use. Friends don't make you rich.

Narrator When he was a teenager, he never seemed to have any girl friends, either. His parents got quite worried.

Mum Why don't you ask Rachel to the theatre with you?

Ebenezer What? Have you seen the price of theatre tickets, Mum? No, I'll just stay in and count my money.

Narrator Soon, Ebenezer had quite a lot of money, but he always thought that being rich meant having more! Gradually, his friends got married. He used to see them in their gardens, playing with their children.

Ebenezer I'd like some children, but families cost money.

Narrator So Ebenezer just had to resign himself to never having a family of his own. Instead, he bought a farm.

Ebenezer People will always need food – and they'll pay for it!

Narrator One year, Ebenezer had a big crop. While he was wondering what to do with it all, the Mayor called.

• he *walked up the path*

- and he *knocked on the door*
- and he gave Ebenezer *a big smile*

Ebenezer	*(Aside)* Oh, good! I bet he's come to tell me that I've been made 'Businessman of the Year'.
Mayor	I expect you know why I've come to see you.
Ebenezer	*(Pretending to be casual)* No, I really can't imagine what you'd want with a humble person like me.
Mayor	Well, you've had a really terrific crop, haven't you?
Ebenezer	Yes, I have.
Mayor	You must be about the most successful businessman in the town, so we thought . . .
Ebenezer	*(Aside)* Here it comes. I must try to look surprised
Mayor	. . . that you might give some food to the poor people.
Ebenezer	What! How will I get rich if I do silly things like that?
Mayor	B-b-but you already *are* rich, Ebenezer.
Ebenezer	Nonsense! I've got to be a lot better off before I'm rich.
Mayor	But you haven't got big enough barns for all that food.
Ebenezer	Then I'll build bigger ones! I'll store up all the food so that I can get rich without having to work for it! What a cheek! Just because those silly people chose to have families, and wasted money on their friends, they expect me to help them when they're poor!
Narrator	That night, Ebenezer had a terrible shock. He died. No-one was there to hold his hand, and no-one came to his funeral. Poor, sad Ebenezer died as he'd lived – alone. He never got to eat all that lovely food, and he never enjoyed being rich, because to him 'rich' always meant 'better off than I am now'. Poor, sad Ebenezer!

Airs and Graces

Based on Luke 14:7-11

Narrator Tom was really excited. He had been invited to the wedding of the famous concert pianist, Roland F. Sharpe, to the operatic soprano, Edwina G. Flatte. They were a lovely couple, and everyone said how natural they were together.

- Tom *combed his hair*
- and he *tied his tie*
- and he *straightened his buttonhole*

Tom I've got to look smart. After all, I'm bound to be on the top table; I was an old college friend of Roland.

Mother That's the first I knew of it. When was that?

Tom You know, Mother. During my Academy days when I was a violinist.

Mother Your 'Academy days'? You're exaggerating a bit, aren't you? And you weren't a violinist, either.

Tom Yes I was.

Mother You worked in the canteen.

Tom I'd have been a student, but they just didn't seem to recognise my talent.

Mother Couldn't seem to find it, more likely! Now, Tom, you won't give yourself airs and graces, will you?

Tom I told you, we're real mates, old Roly and me.

Narrator Meanwhile, in a different part of the town, Richard was also getting ready to go. He couldn't understand why he'd been invited. He used to work at the academy, too, as the caretaker. Although he'd never learnt to play, he loved to listen to music on his office radio. A lot of the students had very expensive instruments, and – although it wasn't really his job – Richard used to look after them. Well, it was a wonderful wedding, and afterwards Tom went around slapping everyone on the back, and talking about 'old times'.

Tom	It's strange that such clever people seem to have such bad memories, but I don't mind reminding them who I am. Well, better get to the reception.
Narrator	When Tom arrived at the reception, he was really pleased that he was such a special friend of Roly. There were so many tables!
Tom	I'm glad I got here early. Ah, this must be the top table. Better leave a couple of seats for their families – don't want to be pushy.
Narrator	Very soon, the room started filling up and Tom saw the happy couple approaching. Roly had his arm around someone – it was that caretaker fellow, Richard.
Tom	I remember him from my Academy days. Quite a nice man, but of course not one of the 'in' set. He was no musician – all he did was listen to it. Any fool could do that. What's really hard is playing it.
Narrator	You can see why Tom never got accepted as a student.
Roland	Hello. I'm sorry, but I don't think we've met.
Tom	Hi there, Roly baby! Love the sense of humour!
Roland	Oh, yes. *Now* I remember you. Look, I'm sorry – this is rather embarrassing – this place is for Richard here. You remember Richard, don't you. He was always so helpful – and *such* a musician! There's a place for you over there near the entrance.
Narrator	Tom couldn't believe what he was hearing. Everyone else seemed to find it very amusing, for some reason. Then Tom noticed something else that was strange. They all seemed to know Richard, and to like him, and to want to talk to him. Tom couldn't understand it. But then, that was poor Tom's whole trouble, you see. He just couldn't understand what was really important in life, and what wasn't.

Don't Be Taken In

Based on Luke 16:1-9

Narrator   Jake was personal accountant to a man called Zebedee One evening, Jake was counting Zebedee's money.

Jake   Two for Zebedee, one for me. Two for Zebedee, one for me. Two for Zebedee, one for me.

Narrator   You may think that's a strange way to count money, and Jake's friend Mark, the butler, didn't approve either.

Mark   That's Zebedee's money. You've got no right to take it.

Jake   Oh go polish your halo! Two for Zebedee, one for me.

Mark   Zebedee's a good boss. I can't stand by and see him being cheated by someone he trusts.

Narrator   Now Mark didn't like gossip, but the more he thought about it the more he knew that he had to tell Zebedee.

Mark   I hope you don't think I'm prying, sir, but do you actually know how much money you've got?

Zebedee   It's not your business. Anyway, I leave all that to Jake.

Mark   Well, I'd do a bit of checking if I were you, sir.

Narrator   Zebedee was not pleased, and he sent for Jake.

Zebedee   I don't know exactly what's been going on, but I mean to find out. I'm going away for a few days, and when I come back I'm going through the accounts.

Narrator   Zebedee went away; Jake stayed home and worried.

- he *bit his nails*
- and he *scratched his head*
- and he *wrung his hands*

Jake   Oh dear! What am I going to do if I lose this job? I'm no good at heavy work, and I'm far too proud to beg.

Narrator	Jake sent for everyone who owed Zebedee money.
Jake	Tell me, Luke, How much do you owe Zebedee?
Luke	Er – a thousand gallons of olive oil, I'm afraid.
Jake	That's a lot of olive pips! Let's call it five hundred.
Luke	Well, it's very kind of you I'm sure. If ever there is anything you need, you just ask me and I'll help you.
Jake	I'll remember. Now, Sam – how's the bakery going?
Sam	Look, I know I owe you for that hundred kilos of wheat, but I'm afraid I simply can't pay you.
Jake	Let's call it fifty kilogrammes – would that help?
Sam	Oh, ever so much! I'm really very grateful. And if I can ever help you at all, you only have to ask.
Narrator	Can you see what Jake is up to?
Jake	Hello, Jack – how's the catering trade?
Jack	I'm not paying that ridiculous bill for wine!
Jake	I don't think you'd get it cheaper anywhere else.
Jack	At one of the weddings I did, we ran out of wine and a guest made some more out of plain water. Now if he can do that, how come you have to charge so much?
Jake	Look, why don't we just mark your account as paid?
Jack	Fair enough. Let me know if I can help you any time.
Narrator	When Zebedee came back Jake knew he was going to give him the sack, so he resigned. All the people in the town loved him and wanted to help him out. All, that is, except Mark who knew what had been going on.
Mark	If I've got the choice between a clever person and an honest one, give me the honest one every time.

Ben and Neb get Better

Based on Luke 17:11-19

Narrator I want to introduce you to two friends, called Ben and Neb. They were as opposite as their names. Ben was from Galilee and Neb was from the next county, called Samaria. Their problem was that they had a very nasty disease which made them come out in a rash all over. Everybody was afraid of catching it, and so they drove Ben and Neb away. They didn't belong anywhere, and they lived right on the border so that whenever anybody started throwing stones at them they could just nip across the border and get away. One day, Ben and Neb met up with some other people like themselves. There were eight of them, including a woman called Rachel.

Rachel We're looking for Jesus. He heals people.

Narrator Ben and Neb joined up with Rachel and her group, and soon they saw Jesus who was with his friends.

Neb He won't want to know – not with his friends around.

Rachel I had a friend called Joe once, who was worse than any of us, and Jesus touched him.

Ben You're the one that's touched if you believe that!

Rachel You can scoff if you like, but it's true. Joe told me himself.

Neb Why don't we just shout to him from where we are? Then if he doesn't want to get too close he can say so.

Rachel Fair enough. Hey, Jesus! Over here! Can you help us?

Jesus Go and show yourselves to the priests.

Ben Fat lot of good that is! The priests put us here in the first place – they'll just chase us away again.

Rachel Just a minute – I think I know what it's about. Let's go.

Neb Don't be silly, there's no point.

Rachel	Yes there is. Trust me! Sorry – I meant trust Jesus.
Narrator	Rachel set off, and gradually the rest followed
Ben	I bet Jesus is having a good laugh at us – and I'm not being made a fool of by anyone.
Narrator	Ben was very angry, and as he spoke:

- he *waved his arms*
- and he *thumped his palm*
- and he *wagged his finger in Rachel's face*

Rachel	Hey, Ben! Look at your finger!
Ben	Don't change the subject!
Rachel	No, really! Look – the skin's healthy. And your face as well.
Narrator	Ben stopped yelling and looked. It was true. His hands and arms were healthy as though he'd been given a completely new skin.
Ben	Your face is better, too. We've all been healed!
Rachel	Come on, let's go to the priests.
Neb	Shouldn't we go and thank Jesus, first?
Rachel	Oh, he'll be long gone by now.
Ben	Anyway, the priests are far more important than Jesus.
Narrator	So off they went – or at least, nine of them did. Neb went back and found Jesus, and thanked him.
Jesus	Isn't that interesting? Ten were healed, but only one says thank you – and he's the last one you'd have expected to. You know, the people who are called 'outsiders' are often the ones with real faith.

Keep Your Wig On, Judge!

Based on Luke 18:2-5

Narrator   Gabriella's husband had died and she was left alone with her daughter, Becky. Sam, the greedy landlord, wasn't very nice about it.

Sam   It's not my fault your husband's dead. If I reduce the rent I might end up poor and pathetic like you.

Narrator   Gabriella didn't know what to do. Then she got a job as a cleaner. The work was quite hard and very badly paid. Becky thought it was all Sam's fault.

Becky   If you paid less rent, you'd need less money.

Gabriella   Sam owns all the houses, so he can set his own rents.

Narrator   That afternoon, when they were out for a walk, they saw a man who was wearing really funny clothes.

Becky   Why's he wearing a wig? Hasn't he any hair?

Gabriella   Yes, but he's a very important person. He's a judge.

Becky   Oh, do important people have to look silly?

Gabriella   You mustn't talk like that about people.

Becky   What does a judge do, then?

Gabriella   He settles arguments and makes people behave fairly.

Becky   Hey, mister Judgy person, can you help my mum, and stop her landlord charging so much rent – and I promise I won't say your wig looks silly ever again.

Judge   Take this abominable child home and teach her to be polite to important men, you dreadful, scruffy woman.

Gabriella   She's not abominable, and these are my work clothes. I'd rather be scruffy than rude. Come on, Becky.

Narrator   Gabriella was surprised at herself.

Gabriella	I shouldn't have done that. Just because someone's rude doesn't mean it's right to be rude back.
Becky	Well, I think he should help you.
Gabriella	You may be right. I'll go and see him one day.
Judge	Why should I help you? You and your horrible child!
Gabriella	That's not the point. Sam's charging too much rent.
Judge	Go away, Sam is a good respectable citizen. And he's very rich. We need rich people in this town a lot more than we need poor spongers like you.
Narrator	Gabriella decided the judge was going to do the right thing, whatever it took. Every day, she went and hammered on his door. Then she stood outside with a big poster saying, 'Sack the unjust judge'. Soon other women, joined her and started chanting,

- *'Fair rents for all!'*
- *'Fair rents for all!'*
- *etc.*

Eventually, the judge called Sam to see him.

Judge	You'll have to lower your rents.
Sam	If I do that you'll have to reduce your cut.
Judge	Shut up! D'you want the whole town to hear? Look, I've had enough of being pestered by this woman. Either you reduce your rents or we'll get the inspectors in to check your houses over.
Sam	Oh, don't do that! I'll cut the rents.
Judge	Now will you women leave me alone?
Gabriella	Well, we're very pleased about the rents, but we think we ought to talk to you about fair wages for cleaners.

Representation and Reality
Based on Luke 18:9-14

Narrator   It was Sunday again, and Tony felt guilty. Everyone kept telling him that Christians should enjoy Sundays.

Tony   *Real* Christians enjoy worship. What's wrong with me? I bet Harry Snooks will be there today, as usual.

Narrator   Harry was a Real Christian: he was so good it hurt! Everyone knew how good Harry was, because Harry was always telling them. Every week, he was at the Prayer Meeting, the Bible Study and the Evangelisation Strategy and Co-ordination Committee – known among a few irreverents as Bible Bashers Anonymous.

Tony   What I really dread is the 'Open Prayer' slot in the service. One week, I spent most of Saturday writing a prayer out, and plucked up courage to use it on Sunday. Afterwards, Harry told me off for reading it.

Harry   Real Prayer has to come straight from the heart.

Tony   But it did. I worked really hard at getting it right.

Harry   Real Prayer doesn't need to be thought about. You just know what to say.

Narrator   Perhaps it would help if Tony attended the midweek meetings like Harry did, but it was terribly difficult. Apart from his family commitments, there was his prison visiting and his work for Mencap – and he couldn't let all those people down. Tony had even begun to ask questions about how true it all was.

Tony   If there's a God, why's he so concerned about the kind of prayers we use but not about the other things I'm doing? Doesn't God care about the prisoners?

Narrator   • Harry *shook his head*
• then he *shrugged his shoulders*
• then he *pointed his finger at Tony*

Harry	They shouldn't have got in trouble in the first place.
Narrator	When Tony arrived at the church this Sunday he found a seat just inside the door, right at the back. The service started and they sang some very jolly songs, but that just made Tony feel worse. Then they came to the 'Open Prayer Time', and Tony was feeling ill.
Harry	Thank you, God for helping me to be a Real Christian. I could never have given four thousand pounds to the church if you hadn't strengthened me. And I thank you for making me so good with words, so that I always say such great prayers. And thank you, God, for reserving me a good place in heaven.
Narrator	By the time Harry got to the end, Tony was feeling worse than ever. Suddenly he did an amazing thing.
Tony	*(Loudly)* God forgive me for being such a bad person!
Narrator	There was a deathly silence. Tony just sat there, thinking what a fool he had made of himself. When the service ended, a group of people gathered around him. Tony thought he was in for a telling off for spoiling the service, but they all seemed to like him!
Worshipper 1	What a wonderful prayer! Simple and to the point.
Worshipper 2	Absolutely sincere,
Narrator	Tony found that he had a lot of friends -- including Joan, who was a Pillar Of The Church.
Joan	Why d'you think you're so bad? Everyone in the town loves you because of the way you help people.
Narrator	Tony couldn't believe it. Then he noticed Harry standing all alone in a corner of the room, and felt sorry for him. The two men walked home together, and Harry seemed a lot quieter and less sure of himself.
Tony	Are you all right?
Harry	Yes – but I just wish I could be a bit more like you.

Noncommittal Nick

Based on John 3:1-8

Narrator   There was a man called Nicodemus who was a member of the Jewish Council – a bit like being a Member of Parliament today. Like a lot of politicians, he thought he could talk his way through life with no problem. He prided himself on always seeing both sides of a question, which is good. What he couldn't understand, though, was that even if you see both sides, you sometimes have to make a choice. You can't go on for ever trying to face in two directions at once.

Nicodemus   I'm very proud of being on the Council. I've got a lot of power, people respect me, and I enjoy the council meetings, when we discuss terribly important things.

Narrator   Now at that time, Jesus was saying that being rich and powerful wasn't important. That worried Nicodemus, and he went to Jesus at night, so that his friends wouldn't see. He was very furtive.

- he l*ooked to the left*
- and he *looked to the right*
- and he *beckoned with his finger*

Nicodemus   Excuse me, Jesus, I do hope I'm not bothering you but you're such a good person – and we know you must be God's messenger because you do the most wonderful, amazing, simply superfantapendous things . . .

Jesus   Oh dear! A politician – you can always tell them. Look, if you want to follow me it'll mean a complete change of life. Like being born all over again.

Nicodemus   What?' I'm a bit big for that now you know.

Jesus   It's the truth, You've got to leave the old life behind, just like being born again. You can't compromise on it.

Narrator   Now I think Nicodemus understood exactly what Jesus was saying, but he didn't like it, and so he played dumb.

Jesus   Look, Nicodemus, the world can offer you wonderful things: power, money, influence, but none of that lasts for ever. If you want the really important things, the world can't give you those. Only God can. That's why you can't compromise. Go on, Nicodemus – let God change your life!

Nicodemus That sounds wonderful. What do I have to do?

Jesus Just let go. Stop trying to compromise and hang onto all the money and power. Stop worrying about what your friends will think or whether you'll be able to afford nice clothes. Let go of all that, and let God change your life.

Nicodemus Well, I'd like to of course, but it's not that simple. I've got a family, and a big house. And I'm someone who's respected in the neighbourhood. You can't expect me to give all that up.

Jesus That's the point. Life with God is never clear-cut and easy. It's like the wind. You hear it blowing, but you never quite know where it's come from or where it's going. That's how it is with the life God gives.

Narrator Nicodemus was unhappy. He could tell Jesus and his friends had a better kind of life than he did, for all his money and power. He could see that what Jesus was doing really meant something. And in his heart of hearts he really did care about the people Jesus helped. But he just couldn't bring himself to make a commitment.

Nicodemus After all, what's wrong with a bit of compromise? If I keep my money and my position, I can help those poor people – but it doesn't mean I've got to be one of them.

Narrator So Nicodemus went sadly on his way. And Jesus stood there, just as sadly, and watched him go. After all, God doesn't want to force anybody to live his life – even though it would be wonderful if everyone did! That wasn't the end of the story for Nicodemus. He carried on battling with himself for a long time before he finally made his choice. Poor old Noncommittal Nick!

Back to the Good Old Days!

Based on John 11:1-44

Narrator   Martha and Mary were friends of Jesus who lived with their brother Lazarus at Bethany. One day, Martha was just finishing scrubbing the front step.

Mary   Martha, I'm worried. Lazarus doesn't seem well.

Martha   Oh, he's okay. Careful – I've just cleaned that!

Mary   I really think it's serious. I'm calling the doctor

Martha   Well make sure he wipes his feet when he arrives.

Doctor   I'm terribly sorry, but he's not going to get better.

Martha   Really, Mary! Why didn't you tell me about this before? *(To doctor)* You haven't tried hard enough! Get to work, and don't stop until you've cured him.

Mary   I know! Let's send for Jesus.

Narrator   Mary sent a message to Jesus. He sent back a note saying, that he'd be along in a few days and not to worry. But Lazarus died before Jesus got there

Martha   I know Jesus is busy, but he should have come.

Mary   He's never been too busy for his friends, though, Martha. I just don't understand what's going on.

Narrator   Meanwhile, Jesus knew Lazarus had died.

Jesus   It's time to go to Bethany.

Narrator   His disciples thought it was dangerous. Bethany was near Jerusalem. But Thomas persuaded them.

Thomas   It might be dangerous, but Jesus is always there for us if we're in trouble. I'm with him.

Narrator   Martha heard Jesus was on his way and went to meet him.

Martha   Wherever have you been? If you'd been here, Lazarus wouldn't have died. Is this the thanks I get for all the cooking and cleaning I do for you? *(Pause)* I'm sorry, Jesus, I know that even now you can ask God for anything and he will give it to you.

Jesus   Lazarus will live, Martha. Do you believe that?

Martha   Oh, I believe we'll see him in heaven, but that's going to be a long wait.

Jesus   Trust me. New life is my business.

Martha   Mary will want to see you. I'll get her.

Mary   Why didn't you come when I sent for you? I know you could have saved him.

Narrator When Jesus saw his friends crying, he cried as well. Then he went with them to the grave, which was a cave with a heavy stone in front of it.

Jesus   Open the grave.

Martha   What? After four days? Ugh!

Jesus   Haven't you heard anything I've said to you? Open the grave and you'll see just how great God is.

Narrator So they rolled the stone away

Jesus   Lazarus! Come out of there!

Narrator They heard scuffling sounds from inside the cave, and then Lazarus appeared at the entrance.

- he *blinked in the sun*
- and he *yawned*
- then he gave a *big stretch*

Jesus   Why doesn't one of you stop staring and help him? Take that awful shroud off, for a start.

Mary   Now everything can be the way it used to be.

Jesus   Yes, back to the old life with all its joys and its sorrows. But stick with me, and you'll see something a lot more exciting than that.

Breakfast on the Beach
Based on John 21:1-23

Narrator   Peter should have been very happy, because Jesus had risen from the dead, but he was fed up. He and his friends had fished all night and caught nothing. Then they heard a voice calling to them.

Jesus   *(From a distance)* Have you caught anything?

Peter   Did you hear something, John?

John   It was that guy on the beach, Peter. I can't see who he is, though.

Peter   *(Calls back)* Not a blooming thing!

Jesus   Try the other side of the boat.

Peter   What does he know? He's just some landlubber walking his dog, I expect!

John   Perhaps he can see something we can't. Let's try.

Narrator   So they threw the net out on the other side.

Peter   Perishing amateurs – stand safely on the beach and tell us how to do our – hey, what's going on?

Narrator   The net was full of fish – the biggest catch ever!

John   I know! That's Jesus – he's pulled that stunt before!

Narrator   Joyfully, Peter jumped out and waded to the shore.

John   That's right, leave us to do the hard work!

Narrator   Eventually, they emptied the net on the beach.

John   Every kind of fish you can think of is in here!

Jesus   There's room for all kinds as far as I'm concerned.

Narrator   Jesus lit a fire and started to cook breakfast.

John   This is very odd: he's the leader, but he serves us.

Jesus	Simon, son of John, are you my best friend?
Narrator	Peter didn't like being called Simon. Jesus had given him a new name, 'Peter: the Rock' – a sign of how strong he was. So why call him Simon?
Peter	Of course I am – you know that.
Jesus	Then look after my other friends.
Narrator	Peter thought this was very strange talk.
Jesus	Simon, son of John, are you my friend?
Peter	Of course I am, Jesus. You know I'm your friend.
Jesus	Then take care of the others
Narrator	Peter was very puzzled now. But it wasn't over.
Jesus	Simon, son of John, are you my friend?
Peter	Of course, I am! You know that perfectly well!
Jesus	Then care for the rest.
Narrator	Peter was getting thoroughly confused. Why had Jesus asked three times? Then he remembered.

- he *looked very sad*
- and he *hung his head*
- and he *started to cry*

Peter	Oh of course! I let him down! Three times!
Jesus	Don't be too upset, Peter. If you don't face up to things you can't deal with them.
Peter	What about John – what's he going to do?
Jesus	That's none of your business. Why, even if I asked him to wait here until the end of time – even then, it would still be no concern of yours, would it?
Narrator	That did it! A rumour started flying around that John would never die. But that wasn't what Jesus said at all, was it?

Wait for the Power

Based on Acts 2:1-21

Narrator Jesus had gone back to heaven, leaving his friends to carry on his work. He'd told them not to start straight away but to stay in Jerusalem until he gave them the power they needed. Peter was getting impatient.

Peter It's all very well, Matthew, but the city is full of people. We shan't have another chance like this for nearly a year. We should be telling people about Jesus.

Matthew Jesus told us to wait. I know all about waiting – when I was a tax man, people kept me waiting for months. Anyway, we'd need to know dozens of different languages – wouldn't we, Thomas?'

Thomas Let's be honest. We don't really want to go out there, anyway. There are people who want to kill us, and I'm too young to die – come to think of it, I always will be.

Narrator As usual, Thomas was the most honest one of the group. In their hearts, everybody knew that he was right. That was why they'd bolted themselves in.

Peter Close the window, Andrew. Sounds like the wind's getting up.

Andrew It's already closed . We nailed it up for security.

Peter Well you didn't do it properly.

Narrator Thomas didn't think it was the wind, anyway.

- he *licked his finger*
- and he *held it up in the air*
- and he *shook his head*

Thomas It's not the wind. I can't feel any draught at all.

Narrator All the disciples sat very quietly and listened. The noise got louder, but the air was still.

Thomas   Hey, Peter! Your hair's on fire!

Peter   Don't be daft! I'd know if my hair was on fire. You're the one who's got that problem.

Narrator   Then they realised that there seemed to be flames over everybody's head. Suddenly, they unbolted the door and went rushing out into the street and started telling everyone that Jesus was alive – and all of a sudden they were language experts! Andrew was speaking in Persian to a group of carpet merchants, while Philip had cornered a couple of soldiers and was talking in Latin, and Thomas – who had always doubted the importance of learning languages – was busy winning an argument with some philosophers, in Greek.

Peter   This is silly. We could get ourselves into serious trouble doing this. Still, some things are worth getting into trouble for – and this is important.

Narrator   That morning, thousands of people heard the good news that Jesus was alive. The religious authorities didn't like it because they were afraid of losing their power. So they went around saying that Peter and his friends were drunk.

Peter   Do me a favour! At this time of the morning? This is the power of God at work, but you're too bothered about yourselves to recognise it.

Narrator   Then the disciples realised that this was the 'power' Jesus had promised them. They knew there would still be hard and dangerous times ahead because Jesus had told them that, too. But they knew it was worth it. Now they understood that, whatever happened, Jesus would always be with them and God wouldn't let their lives or their work be wasted. Now that's what I call power!

A Disciple in the Desert

Based on Acts 8:26-39

Narrator Philip, who was one of Jesus' friends, was in Jerusalem for the annual festival. Jesus had gone back to heaven a few weeks before, but his friends knew that he was still with them although they couldn't see him. So Philip was wondering whether there was anything particular that Jesus wanted him to do

Philip I think I'll go for a walk. All the celebrations are getting a bit heavy and I fancy somewhere quiet. So if anyone wants me I'll be along the Gaza Road.

Narrator Also in Jerusalem was Jim. He was the chief adviser to the queen of Ethiopia. He had come to Jerusalem for the festival, but now it was time to go home. Before he set out, though, there was one more thing he had to do: buy himself a souvenir, such as a nice piece of Jerusalem Rock. But Jerusalem Rock is not the same as Blackpool Rock!

- he tried to *bite a piece off*
- then he *licked it*
- and then he *pulled a horrible face*

Jim Ugh! This may be fine for building temples on, but you can't eat it. And I'm not mad about silly chariot stickers saying 'I've been to Jerusalem', either. I know – I'll buy myself a Bible. It will remind me of my visit, and I'll have something to read on the journey home.

Narrator So he bought his Bible and went back to where his servant was keeping an eye on the chariot.

Jim That's it, we can go home now. You drive, Josh, and I'll have a read.

Narrator As it happened, Jim opened his Bible at a story called *The Suffering Servant*. He felt very sorry for this servant who seemed to be having a terribly hard time, but he was also puzzled, wondering who the person could be. What Jim needed was someone to explain it to him. Just then, Josh noticed something.

Josh   There's some chap walking on the road. D'you think he's lost?

Jim   Stop and see if we can help. Oh, he's coming over.

Philip   Good morning! Are you enjoying your book?

Jim   Yes, very much, but I don't really understand it.

Philip   I think I can probably explain it to you.

Jim   Oh, that's wonderful! Can I give you a lift?

Narrator Philip got into the chariot and Josh started driving again while Philip and Jim read together.

Jim   What I want to know is whether this writer is writing about himself or somebody else.

Philip   It's a prophecy that's only recently come true, about Jesus who loved people so much that he died for them.

Narrator Then Philip went on and told Jim all about his friend Jesus, who had died, risen again and gone back to heaven, but had promised always to be with them.

Jim   How do I become a friend of Jesus, like you?

Philip   Be baptised. It's a sign that you want to make a new start – like being washed clean.

Jim   Well, here's some water, so you can baptise me now.

Narrator After Philip had baptised Jim, he was just wondering what he should do next when God whisked him off somewhere else. There were still lots of other people who wanted to hear about Jesus.

About Turn!

Based on Acts 9:1-22

Narrator   Just after Jesus had gone to heaven, his disciples were telling everyone about him. A religious leader called Saul thought they had to be stopped.

Saul   We must root out these Christians and kill them.

Narrator   Before long, it simply wasn't safe to be a Christian at all, and yet people still kept on joining. Deep in Saul's mind, a niggling little voice told him he might be wrong.* So he worked even harder to try and pretend that the voice wasn't there.

Saul   Kill the Christians! Horrible people with their terrible ideas! Got to kill all of them!

Narrator   So he became really vicious, and went rampaging around chasing Christians and getting them killed. Then, one day, someone told him about a group of Christians at a town called Damascus.

Saul   What! Surely it hasn't spread as far as that! We've got to stop it before it goes any further.

Narrator   He makes it sound like a nasty disease, doesn't he? In a way that's what he thought it was – and the people were the germs that had to be killed. Paul asked for an appointment with the High Priest.

Saul   This new religion has spread to Damascus. If we don't stop it, it will be all over the world.

High Priest   It's very worrying, I agree. What will happen to people like us if this new religion takes over? We could end up just like ordinary people!

Narrator   The High Priest shuddered at the very thought of being 'ordinary'.

High Priest   What d'you think we should do?

Saul   Give me a warrant with your seal on it, and I'll take a few heavies with me and deal with them.

Narrator The High Priest signed the warrant, and Saul went and got his mob together. Then they set off for Damascus.

Saul We'll show them who's really in charge of things!

Narrator Suddenly, a bright light flashed from the sky. Saul did the only thing he could think of: he hit the deck! Then he heard a voice, and this time he couldn't ignore it.

Jesus Saul, Saul, why are you persecuting me?

Narrator Saul was terrified.

- he *covered his eyes*
- then he *put his fingers in his ears*
- then he tried to do *both at the same time!*

Saul Who are you?

Jesus Don't give me that, Saul! You've been trying to ignore me for months. I'm Jesus, the one you're being so nasty to – because when you hurt my friends you hurt me, too.

Saul What shall I do?

Jesus Get up and go to Damascus. You're going to become a Christian and tell everyone about me.

Narrator So Saul got up, but he couldn't see anything.

Saul Gosh! Talk about a blinding light!

Narrator Saul had to be helped by his friends, who couldn't understand what was happening. When they got to Damascus, he was met by a Christian called Ananias.

Ananias I don't know what's going on, but God seems to want me to meet you. I hope you're not going to kill me and my friends.

Narrator Ananias wasn't the only one who was surprised. Imagine the High Priest's face when he found that Saul was a Christian!

* This is not literally spelled out in Scripture, but see Acts 26:14

The Angel, the Apostle and the Great Escape

Based on Acts 12:1-19

Narrator King Herod Agrippa was a rather unpleasant character who seemed to come from a long line of similar nasties. He was terribly unpopular, and so he did what politicians always do – he looked for easy ways of making people like him.

Herod Let me see – a good execution's the thing. The people loved it when I killed that Christian fellow, James. Of course! I can get rid of Christians and make myself more popular both at the same time.

Narrator So he had Peter arrested and used sixteen guards working in four shifts to keep watch on him. One night, Peter was sleeping between two guards with the others keeping watch outside, when he felt a tap on his shoulder. The cell was full of light, and there was an angel standing beside him. Well, he thought it was an angel – or was it?

Angel Hi there, Petey baby! Hey, what are you waiting for? Come along, look lively now, I haven't got all night.

Narrator Peter thought it must be a dream. Well, wouldn't you?

Peter You don't talk like an angel.

Angel Takes all kinds to make a heaven, baby! Now are you coming? I've left a party that's out of this world to come and get you out, so show a leg. Put your coat on, though, 'cos Baby, it's cold outside. Now walk this way, son.

Narrator With that, the angel led the way. He seemed to be hearing music.

- he *snapped his fingers*
- and he *nodded his head*
- and he *swayed from side to side*

Peter thought he might as well enjoy the dream. So he followed the angel out of the prison, past the guards and into the city. The angel was setting a cracking pace

Angel   C'm on, Petey baby – get with that crazy beat!

Narrator   Peter really hoped the dream wouldn't end too soon.

Angel   That's it, Buddy Boy. Gotta go. Wow–ee what a party!

Peter   It's true. God sent an angel to help me. Well, I think he was an angel . . . Yes, of course, Jesus always uses the last people you'd expect. He was an angel!

Narrator   Peter went to the house where Mary lived – no, not that Mary, there were Marys everywhere in those days – with her son, John Mark. Peter knocked on the door, and a maid called Rhoda came to see who it was.

Rhoda   Ello! 'Oo is it?

Peter   It's me. Peter.

Rhoda   Go on! You're 'avin' me on – Peter's in prison, Peter is.

Peter   Oh, come on, Rhoda – it's cold out here!

Rhoda   Ooh it is! It's 'im! 'Ere, missis – Peter's outside!

Mary   Oh, do be quiet, Rhoda. That's a very bad joke.

Rhoda   Honest! I allus know Peter's voice, 'cos 'e talks funny.

Peter   Hey! Rhoda! It's me you silly girl – open the door.

Narrator   Well, you should have seen Mary's face when she came to the door and found it really was Peter. Mind you, that was nothing compared with Herod's face when he discovered that Peter was gone. I'd have loved to have seen it – wouldn't you?